Exercise Your English!

Fourth Class

Breda Courtney Murphy
Edel McCarthy Cronin
Frances Arthur

Contents

Character Study

A character is a person who is represented in a play, a film or a story. A character may also appear as an animal or an imaginary being.

Here are examples of some well-known characters.

Bart Simpson

Gabriella

Princess Fiona

Despereaux

A Match the group of adjectives/phrases to the characters that you think they best describe.

roguish fun-loving disorganised happy-go-lucky friendly	evil cunning power-hungry notorious merciless	mysterious deep-thinking quiet strong-willed determined

Can you think of more adjectives to describe the characters?

B Look at the following characters. Think of adjectives/phrases that you think best describe them, i.e. their personality.

Brain Teaser Make a list of **eight** words that end with the letters '-ddle'.

- **C** is **soft** (**s**) when it is followed by the letters **e**, **i** or **y**, e.g. fa**c**e.
- **G** is usually **soft** (**j**) when it is followed by the letters **e**, **i** or **y**, e.g. **g**iraffe.

A Circle the soft c and soft g in these words.

circus, concert, pigeon, garage, fringe, service
hinge, angelic, tinge, ginger, city, magnificent
cinema, parcel, emergency, recycle, strange, courageous
December, cage, magic, cyclone, stage, German

B Fill in the correct word. Use words from the wordbank in A.

1 The boy was nervous before going on ________.
2 The new release will be shown in the ________ next weekend.
3 People who ________ help the environment.
4 The guards responded quickly to the ________ call.
5 ________ is the last month of the year.
6 I received a ________ in the post.
7 The ________ soldier was awarded for his bravery.
8 The ________ caused a lot of damage to property.
9 The view from the balcony was ________.
10 The dress was green with a ________ of blue.

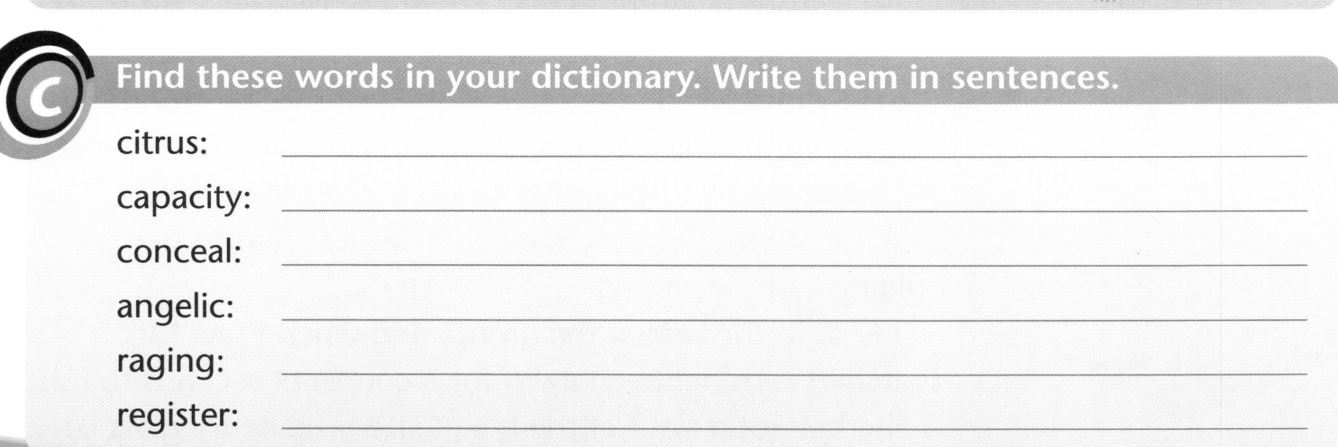

C Find these words in your dictionary. Write them in sentences.

citrus: ________________
capacity: ________________
conceal: ________________
angelic: ________________
raging: ________________
register: ________________

The Great Mouse Plot

Extract from Boy – Tales of Childhood *by Roald Dahl*

My four friends and I had come across a loose floor-board at the back of the classroom, and when we prised it up with the blade of a pocket-knife, we discovered a big hollow space underneath. This, we decided, would be our secret hiding place for sweets and other small treasures such as conkers and monkey-nuts and birds' eggs. Every afternoon, when the last lesson was over, the five of us would wait until the classroom had emptied, then we would lift up the floor-board and examine our secret hoard, perhaps adding to it or taking something away.

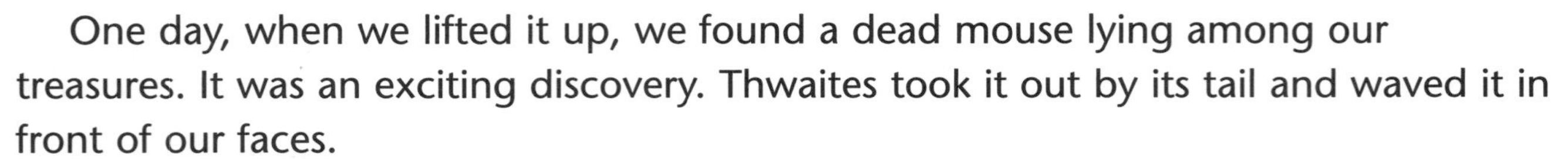

One day, when we lifted it up, we found a dead mouse lying among our treasures. It was an exciting discovery. Thwaites took it out by its tail and waved it in front of our faces.

'What shall we do with it?' he cried.

'It stinks!' someone shouted. 'Throw it out of the window quick!'

'Hold on a tick,' I said. 'Don't throw it away'.

Thwaites hesitated. They all looked at me ...

'Why don't we', I said, 'slip it into one of Mrs Pratchett's jars of sweets? Then when she puts her dirty hand in to grab a handful, she'll grab a stinky dead mouse instead.'

The other four stared at me in wonder. Then, as the sheer genius of the plot began to sink in, they all started grinning. They slapped me on the back. They cheered me and danced around the classroom.

'We'll do it today!' they cried. 'We'll do it on the way home! *You* had the idea,' they said to me, 'so *you* can be the one to put the mouse in the jar.' ...

Thus everything was arranged. We were strutting a little as we entered the shop. We were the victors now and Mrs Pratchett was the victim. She stood behind the counter, and her small malignant pig-eyes watched us suspiciously as we came forward.

'One Sherbet Sucker, please,' Thwaites said to her, holding out his penny.

I kept to the rear of the group, and when I saw Mrs Pratchett turn her head away for a couple of seconds to fish a Sherbet Sucker out of the box, I lifted the heavy glass lid of the Gobstopper jar and dropped the mouse in. Then I replaced the lid as silently as possible. My heart was thumping like mad and my hands had gone all sweaty.

'And one Bootlace, please,' I heard Thwaites saying.

When I turned round, I saw Mrs Pratchett holding out the Bootlace in her filthy fingers.

'I don't want all the lot of you troopin' in 'ere if only one of you is buyin',' she screamed at us. 'Now beat it! Go on, get out!'

As soon as we were outside, we broke into a run. 'Did you do it?' they shouted at me.

'Of course I did!' I said.

'Well done you!' they cried. 'What a super show!'

I felt like a hero. I *was* a hero. It was marvellous to be so popular.

1 Where was the boys' secret hiding place?
2 What sort of treasures did the boys hide under the classroom floor-board?
3 What exciting discovery did the boys make in their hiding place?
4 What did they decide to do with the dead mouse?
5 How did the boys decide who would put the mouse in the jar?
6 What kind of sweets did Thwaites ask for in Mrs Pratchett's shop?
7 Which jar was the mouse dropped into?
8 How did Roald Dahl feel afterwards?

1 Were the boys close friends? Explain your answer.
2 List some other treasures that the boys may have kept in their secret hiding place.
3 Why, do you think, did the boys want to play a trick on Mrs Pratchett?
4 Was it fair that Roald was chosen to put the mouse in the jar?
5 What kind of person was Mrs Pratchett?
6 Describe how Roald felt when he was carrying out the trick.
7 If you were Mrs Pratchett, would you have been suspicious of the group of boys?
8 Write down what you think happened next.

Dictionary Work

Use your dictionary to look up the meaning of the following words. Write a sentence using each word.

prised	hollow	hoard	hesitated
strutting	victors	victim	malignant

Letter Writing

Formal Letters

- Letters requesting or giving information
- Letters of complaint
- Business letters, e.g. letters to the bank

Read this formal letter of complaint.

1 Grimm's Lane
Greytown
Co. Tyrone

7 August 2010

The Manager
Happy Days Hotel
Suntown
Co. Donegal

Dear Miss W. Elcome,

I have been a guest at your hotel on a number of occasions and have always been satisfied with the level of hospitality received. However, I regret to inform you that my most recent stay was very unsatisfactory.

I struggled to the reception desk with my two bulging suitcases where I had to wait ten minutes to be checked in. I had requested a room with a balcony that overlooked the sea but I was given a room overlooking the garden.

I proceeded to the hotel restaurant for my dinner and was appalled to see that there was no ice cream on the dessert menu. At breakfast the next morning, I ordered soft-boiled eggs but when the waiter brought them, they were hard-boiled.

I am hopeful that you will resolve all of these issues before my next visit.

Yours sincerely,
Mrs C. Omplain

1. Write the address of Mrs C. Omplain.
2. Write the address of the hotel.
3. Make a list of all the complaints in the letter.
4. Does Mrs C. Omplain's letter persuade us that the Happy Days Hotel needs to improve its hospitality? Give reasons for your answer.
5. Imagine that you are Miss W. Elcome. Write a formal letter to Mrs C. Omplain, persuading her that your hotel is a great place to stay. Respond to all of the complaints in her letter.

Remember to use **capital letters**:
- at the start of a sentence
- when using 'i' on its own
- for days of the week
- for months of the year
- for special days and festivals.

Place capital letters in the correct places.

1 his birthday is on 25 june.
2 my family and i are going to my aunt's house for christmas day.
3 it rained heavily on monday and tuesday.
4 her sister is getting married on saint valentine's day.
5 james and i go cycling together every saturday.
6 the weather is very cold in january.
7 there is a big parade in town for saint patrick's day.
8 our teacher gave us a test on friday morning.

We must also use **capital letters** for:
- the names of people and their titles, e.g. *Dr Connor, Mrs Smith*
- the names of places, e.g. *Dublin, France.*

Place capital letters in the correct places.

1 my uncle jason plays soccer with me.
2 the capital of england is london.
3 my teacher, mr cronin, is going to africa in july.
4 the weather is much warmer in mexico than in ireland.
5 did you meet mr and mrs clifford yet?
6 mary and lucy are going shopping in limerick on saturday.
7 my mom took me to see dr lynch when i was sick.
8 jenny has a new baby sister named lisa.

Interesting Interviews

Imagine that you are a journalist for your local newspaper. Your job is to conduct an interview with a different person every week and to write that person's profile.

With a partner, discuss the questions you would ask the following people.

- Write down eight questions for each person in your copy.
- Ensure that your questions are suitable for each person and his/her occupation.
- Present your questions to the class.
- Hot Seat! Pretend that you are one of these people. Use your imagination to answer the questions as best you can.

Garda

Aid Worker

Barack Obama

Derval O'Rourke

Choose a well-known person whom you would like to interview. Make a list of questions that you would ask him/her.

Select an older relative or friend to interview. What questions would you ask him/her? Write them down and conduct the interview.

Brain Teaser Name **ten** words that contain the letter z.

- When **ue** comes at the **end** of a word it usually makes the sound **oo** or **ū**, e.g. gl**ue** or aven**ue**.
- When **ue** comes in the **middle** of a word, the word is divided into **two syllables**, e.g. cr**ue**t.

gl**ue**

aven**ue**

cr**ue**t

A Say the words in the wordbank. Write them in the appropriate column.

rescue duel clue duet value gruel statue Sue
fuel cue blue cruel flue continue true

oo sound	**ū sound**	**two-syllable**

- In these words **ei** makes the sound **ā**.

eight **veil**

rein	sleigh	heir	weight	reindeer
neigh	vein	reign	freight	neighbour
their	freighter	weigh	beige	weigh-bridge

B Read the meaning of the word. Write the word from the wordbank above.

1 a tube that carries blood back to the heart ________
2 used to carry Santa's toys ________
3 sound made by a horse ________
4 a colour ________
5 the time during which a king or queen rules ________
6 the person to whom a title or property is left ________
7 ship or aircraft that carries cargo ________
8 a large scale for weighing vehicles ________

A tale of a man against nature

Based on an article by Susan Griffin

***Irish Examiner*, 20 September 2008**

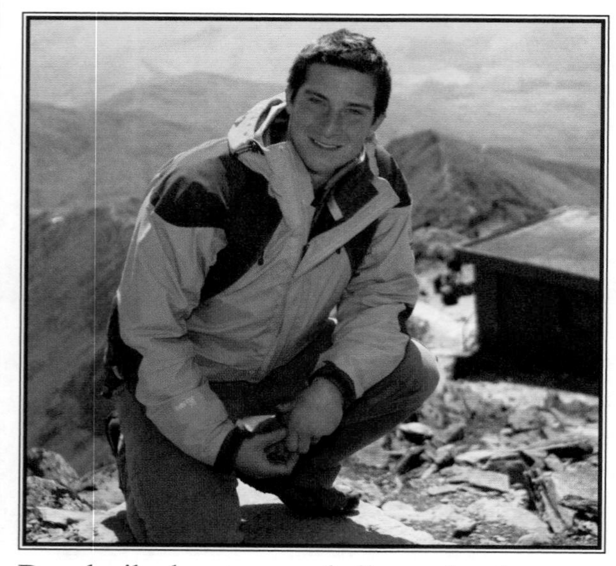

Daredevil adventurer and all-round action man Bear Grylls is best known for parachuting into the world's worst hellholes and surviving on his wits alone. This is a man who's been known to drink the juice from elephant dung to stay hydrated, eat raw zebra to keep hunger pangs at bay and climb inside a dead camel for shelter. Why is just one question that springs to mind.

'I just love climbing mountains and chasing alligators and catching snakes, and surviving,' he says. 'I love all of that. It's what I've done all my life, except I've never been filmed doing it before.'

The son of the late Conservative politician Michael Grylls, Eton-educated Bear, 34, says he's been an adventurer since he was knee-high.

'I was always getting rescued by lifeboats and climbing trees. I think a lot of my identity came from being the only person who could reach the top of that building or that tree. It was definitely a big part of my life growing up.'

Bear joined the Territorial Army after school, and served three years as a survival instructor and patrol medic with the SAS Special Forces Unit. His military career ended after a parachute accident left him with a broken back, but he didn't allow this to deter him from realising his childhood dream of climbing Mount Everest; he fought his way to recovery and two years later, aged 23, he became the youngest Briton to climb it.

Other expeditions followed, including his first major TV show, *Escape To The Legion* … It was the success of this series that led to the filming of his new six-part television series, *Born Survivor*. In it we see Bear tackling the Skeleton Coast of Namibia, the deadly swamps of Louisiana, the desert canyons of Mexico's Baha Peninsula and the rapids of Zambia, finishing with a two-part journey through the Pacific 'Ring of Fire'.

His worst moment?

'Probably being stung by a load of bees. I was trying to get honey out of their nest and they all came back after I smoked them out … I had to do the rest of the show basically blind.'

'I always take a little laminated picture of my wife Shara and my two boys, Jesse and Marmaduke, with me in the sole of my shoe. That comes out when I'm really struggling. But then I love to push the boundaries and I feel we're making the best TV we've ever made and that in itself is a good feeling.'

1. For what is Bear Grylls best known?
2. Name two extraordinary things that Bear did for survival.
3. What career did Bear's father have?
4. What did Bear do after finishing school?
5. Why did Bear's military career end?
6. What did Bear achieve at the age of twenty-three?
7. List the adventures Bear undertakes in his TV series *Born Survivor*.
8. When Bear is struggling, what does he do to help himself along?

1. From the report, make a list of the adjectives that describe Bear.
2. Add your own adjectives to the list in No. 1.
3. Imagine that you were part of the TV crew filming Bear when his 'worst moment' occurred. Write a description of what happened.
4. Use your atlas to locate the following places visited by Bear in his TV series:
   - Namibia
   - Louisiana
   - Mexico's Baha Peninsula
   - Zambia
   - The Pacific Ocean
5. List five other interesting places around the world that Bear could visit and film for his television series.

Match the following words to the correct meaning.

- **hydrate**
- **identity**
- **expedition**
- **Briton**
- **media**
- **swamp**
- **canyon**
- **peninsula**

– a deep valley usually formed by a river
– drenched or submerged ground that is usually overgrown
– a narrow strip of land projecting into a sea or lake
– to take in water
– an organised journey or voyage
– forms of communication that reach large numbers of people, such as newspapers, radio and television
– a native or inhabitant of Britain
– individual characteristics by which a person or thing is recognised

Choose five of the words in C and write a sentence for each one.

A Keeping a Diary

A diary is a daily record of events that happen in a person's life.

Diaries are very useful in providing information about the past. For example, *The Diary of Anne Frank* gives us an insight into what her life was like as part of a Jewish family hiding from the Nazis during the Second World War.

Read this extract from Anne's diary.

Wednesday, 5 April 1944

My dearest Kitty,

For a long time now I didn't know why I was bothering to do any schoolwork. The end of the war still seemed so far away, so unreal, like a fairy tale. If the war isn't over by September, I won't go back to school, since I don't want to be two years behind ...

I finally realised that I must do my schoolwork to keep from being ignorant, to get on in life, to become a journalist, because that's what I want! I know I can write. A few of my stories are good, my descriptions of the Secret Annexe are humorous, much of my diary is vivid and alive, but ... it remains to be seen whether I really have talent ...

Unless you write yourself, you can't know how wonderful it is; I always used to bemoan the fact that I couldn't draw, but now I'm overjoyed that at least I can write. And if I don't have the talent to write books or newspaper articles, I can always write for myself. But I want to achieve more than that. I can't imagine having to live like Mother, Mrs Van Daan and all the women who go about their work and are then forgotten. I need to have something besides a husband and children to devote myself to! I don't want to have lived in vain like most people. I want to be useful or bring enjoyment to all people, even those I've never met. I want to go on living even after my death! And that's why I'm so grateful to God for having given me this gift, which I can use to develop myself and to express all that's inside me!

When I write I can shake off all my cares. My sorrow disappears, my spirits are revived! But, and that's a big question, will I ever be able to write something great, will I ever become a journalist or a writer?

I hope so, oh, I hope so very much, because writing allows me to record everything, all my thoughts, ideals and fantasies ...

So onwards and upwards, with renewed spirits. It'll all work out, because I'm determined to write!

Yours, Anne M. Frank

- How has Anne's life changed since the outbreak of the war?
- What is Anne's opinion of her own writings?
- What are Anne's hopes for the future?

B Write

Read *A tale of a man against nature* (page 12) again. Imagine that you are Bear Grylls. Write a diary entry for a day when you were in the wild.

Remember to include the date!

Think about:

- Where were you?
- Who was with you?
- What was the weather like?
- How did you get there?

- A **sentence** must end with a **full stop**.
- A **question sentence** must end with a **question mark** (?).
- A **comma** is used to separate a list of things,
  e.g. *Mam bought an expensive, new, red dress.*
  (The last adjective in a list does not need a comma.)
  We had pizza, chocolate, popcorn and crisps at the party.
  (In a list, the word before 'and' does not need a comma either.)

A Put a full stop or a question mark at the end of these sentences.

1 Is that your sister playing on the swings
2 I am going to Spain next Saturday
3 Would you like to visit my house
4 Rachel likes to eat vanilla ice cream
5 Did anybody see my pencil
6 Sylvia is from Poland
7 Why do we have to get homework
8 What is the highest mountain in Ireland

B Rewrite the following sentences, using commas.

1 Mark Kevin Joe and Jack are my best friends.
2 I had to buy new pens pencils copies and books for school.
3 Dad used flour milk eggs and sugar to make the pancakes.
4 Melissa plays football soccer tennis and basketball.
5 I saw elephants snakes tigers and lions at the zoo.
6 We bought potatoes fruit vegetables and meat in the shop.
7 Red orange yellow and green are some of the colours in a rainbow.
8 There were cars vans and bikes in the garage.

C Rewrite the following passage, using the correct punctuation.

Hint! There are eleven capital letters, seven full stops and four commas.

kelly woke up early saturday morning the sun was shining in the sky she decided to put on her jeans t-shirt and sandals she had porridge toast and orange juice for her breakfast kelly met ben jill and luke at the park they played on the swings slides and see-saw they had a great time

Silly Old Baboon

There was a Baboon
Who, one afternoon,
Said, 'I think I will fly to the sun.'
So, with two great palms
Strapped to his arms,
He started his take-off run.

Mile after mile
He galloped in style
But never once left the ground.
'You're running too slow,'
Said a passing crow,
'Try reaching the speed of sound.'

So he put on a spurt –
By God how it hurt!
The soles of his feet caught fire.
There were great clouds of steam
As he raced through a stream
But he still didn't get any higher.

Racing on through the night,
Both his knees caught alight
And smoke billowed out from his rear.
Quick to his aid
Came a fire brigade
Who chased him for over a year.

Many moons passed by.
Did Baboon ever fly?
Did he ever get to the sun?
I've just heard today
That he's well on his way!
He'll be passing through Acton at one.

P.S. Well, what do you expect from a Baboon?

Spike Milligan

1 Do you like this poem? Explain your answer.
2 Do you think that the poem is well written? Give reasons for your answer.
3 What is your favourite part of the poem?
4 Choose one scene from the poem and illustrate it.

Imagine that you are providing a commentary for a documentary based on Baboon's attempted flight to the sun. Practise reading the poem aloud and perform it for the class.

- One-syllable words that end in an **'ik'** sound are spelled **ick**, e.g. **kick**.
- Words of more than one syllable that end in an **'ik'** sound are spelled **ic**, e.g. picn**ic**.

kick

picn**ic**

A Write the correct word.

music/musick

bric/brick

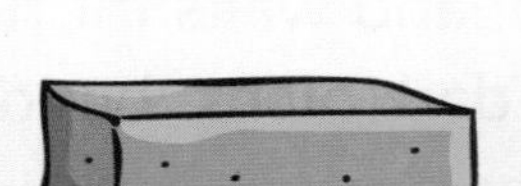

attick/attic

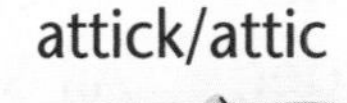

plastick/plastic

trick/tric

thic/thick

comic/comick

traffick/traffic

Atlantic/Atlantick

garlick/garlic

B Read the words. Notice the 'ik' sound at the end. Put eight of these words into sentences. Use your dictionary to help you.

metric	electric	terrific	tragic	logic	tropic
classic	angelic	Pacific	basic	graphic	topic
specific	horrific	mechanic	gigantic	heroic	majestic
athletic	realistic	magic	domestic	Arctic	magnetic

C Fill in the correct word. Use words from the wordbank in B.

1 Polar bears live in the ______________.

2 The ______________ boating accident was most unfortunate.

3 The ______________ action of the garda was rewarded.

4 I had great interest in the ______________ being discussed.

5 The girl is tall, slim and very ______________.

6 The ______________ was unable to repair the car.

7 The hotel is cheap but the facilities are ______________.

8 The film was far-fetched and not very ______________.

9 Care should be taken near an ______________ fence.

10 We use a ______________ system of measurement.

Night Mail

by W.H. Auden

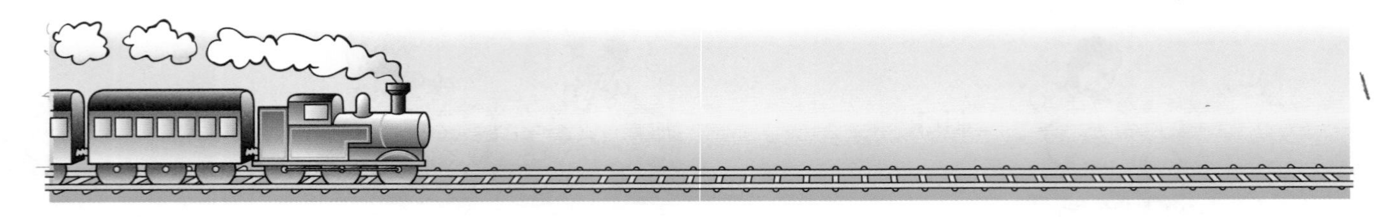

I

This is the night mail crossing the border,
Bringing the cheque and the postal order,

Letters for the rich, letters for the poor,
The Shop at the corner and the girl next door.

Pulling up Beattock, a steady climb –
The gradient's against her, but she's on time.

Past cotton grass and moorland boulder
Shovelling white steam over her shoulder,

Snorting noisily as she passes
Silent miles of wind-bent grasses.

Birds turn their heads as she approaches,
Stare from the bushes at her black-faced coaches.

Sheep-dogs cannot turn her course,
They slumber on with paws across.

In the farm she passes no one wakes,
But a jug in the bedroom gently shakes.

II

Dawn freshens, the climb is done.
Down towards Glasgow she descends
Towards the steam tugs yelping down the glade of cranes,
Towards the fields of apparatus, the furnaces
Set on the dark plain like gigantic chessmen,
All Scotland waits for her:
In the dark glens, beside the pale-green lochs
Men long for news.

III

Letters of thanks, letters from banks,
Letters of joy from girl and boy,
Receipted bills and invitations
To inspect new stock or visit relations,
And applications for situations
And timid lovers' declarations
And gossip, gossip from all the nations,
News circumstantial, news financial,
Letters with holiday snaps to enlarge in,
Letters with faces scrawled in the margin,
Letters from uncles, cousins, and aunts,
Letters to Scotland from the South of France,
Letters of condolence to Highlands and Lowlands,
Notes from overseas to Hebrides –

Written on paper of every hue,
The pink, the violet, the white and the blue,
The chatty, the catty, the boring, adoring,
The cold and official and the heart outpouring,
Clever, stupid, short and long,
The typed and printed and the spelt all wrong.

IV
Thousands are still asleep
Dreaming of terrifying monsters,
Or of friendly tea beside the band at
Cranston's or Crawford's,
Asleep in working Glasgow, asleep in
well-set Edinburgh,
Asleep in granite Aberdeen,
They continue their dreams;
And shall wake soon and long for letters,
And none will hear the postman's knock
Without a quickening of the heart,
For who can bear to feel himself
forgotten?

(Written as a commentary for a G.P.O. film in Britain)

1. In one sentence, write down what the poem is about.
2. List six different types of letters in Verse III of the poem.
3. Select all of the words/phrases in the poem that describe the different landscapes.
4. What placenames are mentioned in the poem?
5. What adjectives come just before Glasgow, Edinburgh and Aberdeen in Verse IV?
6. Does this poem describe long ago or modern times? Give reasons for your answer.

1. Look at a map of Scotland. Locate the placenames mentioned in the poem.
2. Read the poem aloud. What do you notice about the rhythm of each line?
3. Read the poem aloud again, placing emphasis on the first word of each line.
4. What is your favourite part of the poem? Give reasons for your answer.

Close your eyes and listen while your teacher reads the poem aloud.
Now, open your eyes and illustrate a scene from the poem.

Rhyme

Many poems contain words or phrases that rhyme.
Rhyme allows the poet to be descriptive. It also helps us to remember poems and verse more effectively.

Here are some examples of how Spike Milligan uses rhyme in *Silly Old Baboon*.

Mile after mile
He galloped in style…

'You're running too slow'
said a passing crow…

Racing on through the night
Both his knees caught alight…

The following phrases are the first lines of poems. Read them and compose a second line in each. The second line must rhyme with the first line.

Example: If I were a millionaire
I wouldn't have to spare

1. Here comes the spring

____

2. Sammy the soccer star

____

Spike Milligan wrote a humorous poem about a baboon.
Choose an animal and write a poem about it using rhyme.

Use the following to help you to plan your poem:

Animal: _______________

Describing words: _______________

Where you might see this animal: _______________

Words to describe movements/antics: _______________

Rhyming words/phrases: _______________

Title of poem: _______________

Contractions are words that have been shortened.
We put an **apostrophe** (’) where letters have been skipped,
e.g. *he will = he’ll*
do not = don’t

Write the contractions of these words.

you will	she is	we are	it is
I have	had not	he is	we will
was not	they are	I am	will not
you would	cannot	we have	should have

Write these sentences without contractions.

1 They said they’d call later in the evening.
2 We’ve a lot of homework today.
3 ‘You’re not allowed to go to the party,’ said Dad.
4 That’s the boy who didn’t do his homework last night.
5 Dad couldn’t find his car keys this morning.
6 She can’t have dessert until she finishes her dinner.
7 Mike isn’t feeling very well today.
8 You shouldn’t talk to strangers.

Abbreviations are shortened words too. They usually start with a capital letter and need full stops at the end,
e.g. *Estate = Est.*

Note: If the last letter of the shortened word is the same as the last letter of the long word, we do not use a full stop,
e.g. *Doctor = Dr*

Write the full versions of these abbreviations.

(Answers on page 96.)

Tues.	Mrs	Ave	Fr	Dec.
St	Mr	Sr	Tce	Wed.
Co.	Jnr	Snr	No.	km.
Gro.	Est.	Rd	cm.	Oct.

Funny-Sounding Words

Onomatopoeia occurs when a word sounds like what it is describing.

For example:

munch	squash	buzz	hiss

Can you think of any more examples of onomatopoeia?

Idioms (Answers on page 96.)

Many words contain more than one meaning. Also, the way we use words in a sentence can change their meaning.

Read the following phrases. Can you understand what each phrase means? You may discuss them with a partner.

She made a bags of it!

Let's hit the road!

That's a cod!

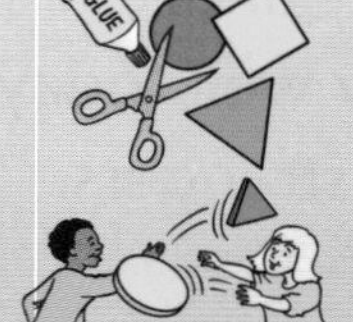

Will we make shapes?

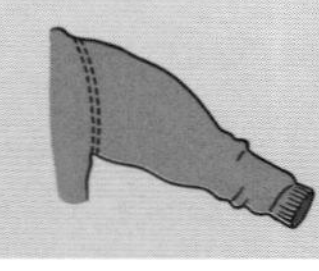

He is a sleveen!

They were throwing shapes.

Unusual Words (Answers on page 96.)

The following list contains funny-sounding words, phrases and placenames. There is one for each letter of the alphabet. You may need some help from your teacher to read some of them. Do you know what they mean? Use your dictionary and the Internet to find out.

abominable
bedraggled
camouflage
Davy Jones' Locker
entrepreneur
flabbergasted
gobbledygook
hobbledehoy
idiosyncrasy
jamboree
kibosh
laughing stock
mackintosh
Nantucket
onyx
paparazzi
quandary
ravioli
sphinx
teenybopper
unique
vamoose
whippersnapper
xylophone
yucca
Zuider Zee

Can you think of other funny-sounding words, phrases or placenames for each letter?

Brain Teaser Make a list of words that rhyme with 'pair'.

Say the word. Fill in the missing letters.

- ar   - er   - or

calend _ _

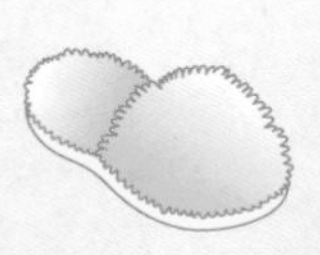

slipp _ _

alligat _ _

ladd _ _

alt _ _

burgl _ _

butt _ _

indicat _ _

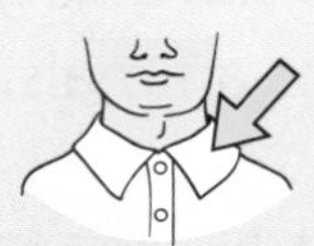

coll _ _

riv _ _

teach _ _

doct _ _

schol _ _

sail _ _

scoot _ _

Add the correct ending to complete the word.

Use your dictionary to help you.

maj _ _	feath _ _	pol _ _
fath _ _	sug _ _	spons _ _
pill _ _	govern _ _	corn _ _
don _ _	may _ _	li _ _
cell _ _	shiv _ _	murd _ _
lett _ _	auth _ _	doll _ _
equat _ _	moth _ _	vineg _ _

Find these words in your dictionary. Write them in sentences.

cedar: ______________________________

juror: ______________________________

glider: ______________________________

senator: ______________________________

editor: ______________________________

conductor: ______________________________

The Amazon River Dolphin

Extract from Where Animals Live *by Mark Carwardine*

There are thirty-seven different dolphins altogether. Dolphins range in size from the tiny Heaveside's dolphin, little more than a metre long, to the famous killer whale, which can grow to over seven metres long. Dolphins have large brains and are very intelligent animals.

There are five different kinds of river dolphin; four of them are named after the river in which they live. Amazon river dolphins are very friendly animals.

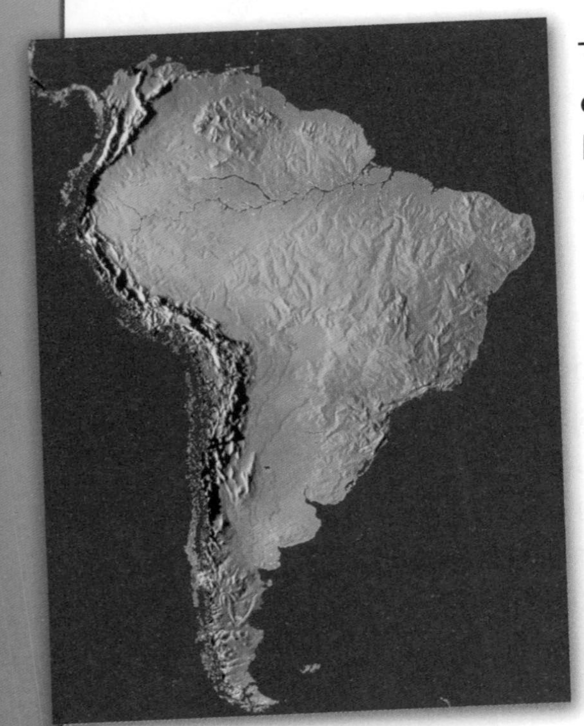

They often come to the aid of injured or troubled companions, even risking danger themselves. They have been seen swimming arm-in-arm, a healthy dolphin on either side of an injured one, regularly carrying it to the surface to breathe.

Little more than two metres long, Amazon river dolphins are very brightly coloured compared with most other members of the dolphin family. The older they are the pinker they become.

In some parts of the Amazon Basin, where they live, they even help the local people. They come to the call of the fishermen, herding fish from deeper water to their nets in the shallows.

They often live in pairs, hunting together for fish, and sometimes crabs and shrimps, which they swallow whole. Baby river dolphins, or calves, are thought to be born between July and September. They are almost half as long as their parents but continue to grow for many years. Like their parents, they have very poor eyesight. They use a form of echolocation – like bats – to find their way around and to catch food.

1 How many different kinds of dolphin are there altogether?
2 What is the name of the smallest dolphin and what size is it?
3 What is the largest dolphin called and what size is it?
4 How do you know that Amazon river dolphins are friendly?
5 Describe the appearance of an Amazon river dolphin.
6 How do the Amazon river dolphins help local people?
7 What do Amazon river dolphins like to eat?
8 How do Amazon river dolphins find their way and catch their food?

True or False?

1 Dolphins have very small brains. ________
2 Dolphins are very intelligent. ________
3 Healthy Amazon river dolphins often help injured dolphins. ________
4 Amazon river dolphins are five metres long. ________
5 Amazon river dolphins become pinker as they grow older. ________
6 Baby Amazon river dolphins are called pups. ________
7 Amazon river dolphins have very good eyesight. ________
8 Bats use echolocation to find their way around and catch food. ________

Use an atlas, a globe or a world map to locate (a) South America and (b) the River Amazon.

There is a rainforest near the River Amazon. There are also rainforests in other places in the world such as parts of Africa and parts of Asia including New Guinea, Borneo and Malaysia.

Read this list. Use books or the Internet to find out which creatures belong to rainforests.

- Shark
- Aye-Aye
- Camel
- Iguana
- Narwhal
- Jaguar
- Poison Arrow Frog
- Scorpion
- Rattlesnake
- Squirrel Monkey

Extension Work

Choose one of the rainforest creatures that you identified in C.

Find out about it and write a paragraph describing it.

Draw a picture to accompany your writing.

Reports

Reports give us information about a topic.

The following are three types of report.

- Critical report – the writer gives his/her opinion of a topic. This opinion may be positive or negative.
- Information-based report – the writer gives factual information about a topic without giving his/her opinion.
- Humorous report – the writer makes the report as lighthearted as possible.

A

The following is a 'brainstorm' that the writer of 'The Amazon River Dolphin' could have used when planning to write about it.

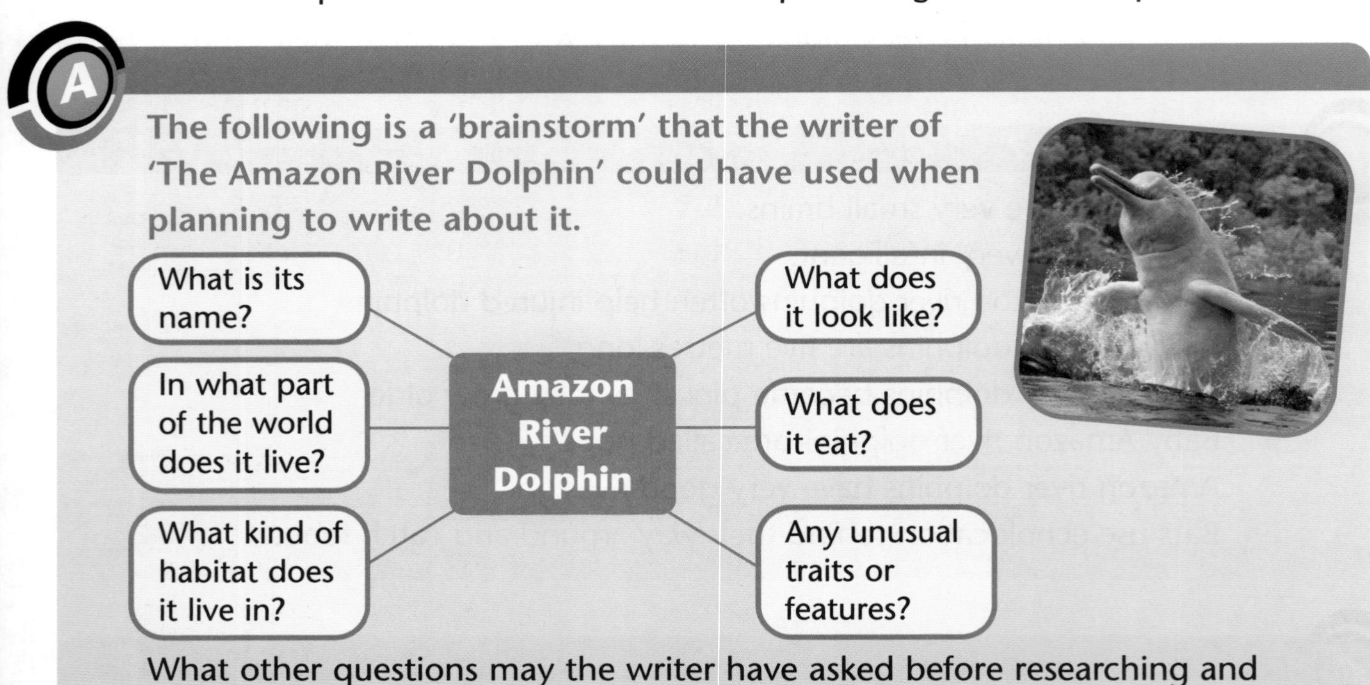

What other questions may the writer have asked before researching and writing about the Amazon River Dolphin?

B

Choose an animal that you would like to research and write a report on it. Use the following headings and K.W.L. chart to help you to plan your report before writing it. Illustrate your report.

Title of report: ______________________________

Who I am writing for: ______________________________

What I will use to find out information: ______________________________

____

K.W.L.

What I know	What I want to know	What I learned
______	______	______
______	______	______
______	______	______

A B C D E F G H I J K L M N O P Q R S T U V W X Y Z

To put words into **alphabetical order** look at the **first letter** of the words. When words start with the **same letter** you must look at the **second letter**. Sometimes you may even have to look at the **third** or **fourth letter**.

Put these words in alphabetical order.

1	dog	snake	cow	horse	pig
2	pink	blue	red	yellow	green
3	banana	plum	melon	grape	orange
4	shirt	skirt	sock	shoe	scarf
5	fish	foot	fridge	flower	fence
6	train	tap	tunnel	tongue	ticket

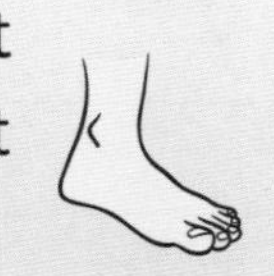

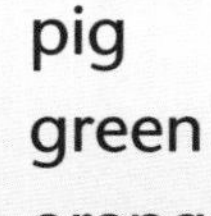

Now put these words in alphabetical order.

1	bed	bench	beard	belt	bell
2	glue	glove	globe	glass	glitter
3	friend	frame	fruit	freezer	frog
4	guitar	gun	guest	guard	gull
5	spine	spill	spire	spice	spike
6	traffic	train	trap	tray	tractor

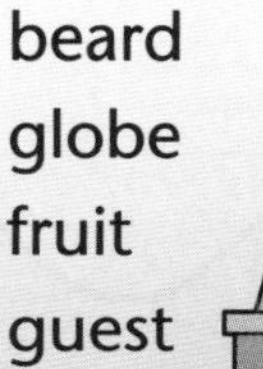
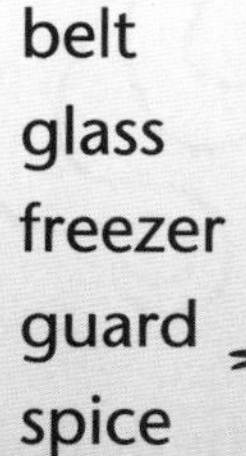

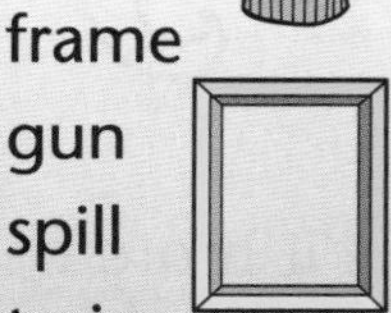

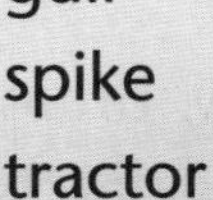

Write these alphabetical lists correctly.

1	jacket	jelly	jockey	jingle	jumper
2	hibernate	hiccup	hill	high	history
3	cone	cook	contest	copy	cord
4	turkey	tulip	turnip	turtle	tuxedo
5	scale	scan	scare	scarf	scalp

Use your dictionary to find a word that will fill the blank in these alphabetical lists.

1	bright	___________	brown	___________	brush
2	rose	rough	___________	row	___________
3	gran	___________	grass	___________	gravity
4	opera	opinion	___________	opposite	___________
5	dance	___________	dark	___________	day
6	salad	sale	___________	sandal	___________

Fun with Words (1)

A Brainstorming

- Think of as many words as you can, associated with the word 'hair'.

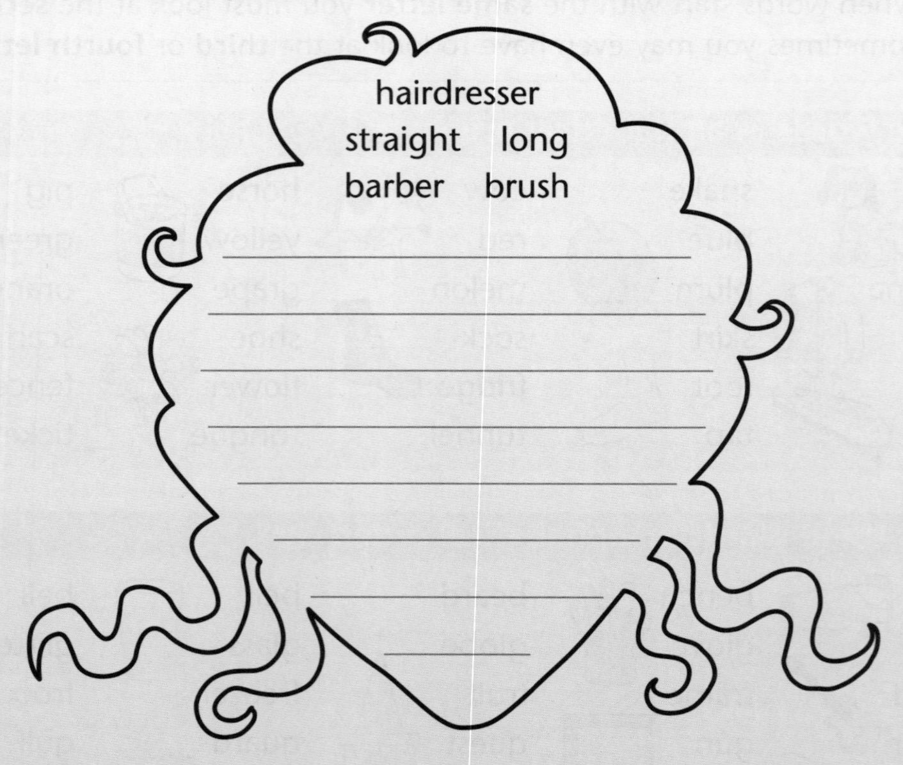

- Now, brainstorm the following topics! Make it more challenging by using a stop-watch. See who gets the most words!

Films Clothes Food Music

B Picture Puzzles (Answers on page 96.)

Look at the following picture puzzles.
Can you work them out?

1

LITTLE	LITTLE
LATE	LATE

2

NEAFRIENDED

3

D D
O O
O O
G G

O O
N N

4

ꓤOOD

5

P H
O O
H P

6

ALL
———
AGAIN

Brain Teaser Answer: Aeroplane. Give **five** possible questions.

Underline the silent letter in each word.

e.g. doub**t**	s**c**ience	**g**nome	g**h**etto	yo**l**k
knife	thistle	answer	debt	scissors
design	exhaust	whistle	wrinkle	knapsack
exceed	limb	ghastly	muscle	wrong
honour	knuckle	salmon	gherkin	kneel
wring	glisten	tomb	exhibit	rhinoceros
foreign	hustle	wrench	palm	knowledge
scent	subtle	almond	mortgage	dinghy

Many words have silent letters.

- **n** is usually silent when it comes after **m**, e.g. autum**n**.
- **gh** is silent in many words, e.g. hi**gh**.

Fill in the correct word.

autumn	high	sigh	fight	delight
hymn	blight	flight	sight	sleigh
column	brought	thought	bought	sought
solemn	eight	weigh	taught	naughty
condemn	daughter	slaughter	distraught	neighbour

1 ___________ is one of four seasons.
2 The ___________ caused the potatoes to rot in the fields.
3 The ___________ child threw a tantrum.
4 The mood of the meeting was ___________.
5 Jockeys must ___________ in before a race.
6 The parents were very proud of their ___________.
7 We invited our ___________ to join us for dinner.
8 The children ___________ games with their money.
9 The injured people were ___________ to hospital by ambulance.
10 The ___________ near the door was painted white.

Read the meaning of the word. Write the word from the wordbank in B.

1 A long, deep-sounding breath = ___________
2 A female child = ___________
3 A large, horse-drawn sledge = ___________
4 Someone who lives near another = ___________
5 A religious song of praise = ___________

The Viking at Drumshee

Extract from The Viking at Drumshee *by Cora Harrison*

Conn is the youngest warrior in Prince Brian Boru's army. They have been living wild in the hills, fighting the invading Vikings, but now the prince has no more money to feed the men. Meanwhile, in their settlement at Limerick, the Vikings have a huge hoard of treasure looted from the abbeys of Ireland – but they guard it closely.

'We'll have to wait until dawn,' said Brian Boru. 'We'll be able to cross the rest of the bog then.' Yes, thought Conn, but at dawn the Vikings will see what we're doing, and they'll be able to send their men around the lake and through the valley at the far side. If only we could cross by night, they would never know which way we're going …

Cautiously he moved one foot, sliding it along the wet mud and then pressing, at first gently, then shifting his whole weight onto it. It held. He moved his other foot, again sliding it until he felt firm ground under it. Then the right foot again. He was definitely on the path. Hope began to rise in him. Perhaps by some instinct he was still going the correct way, keeping to the right path. Excitedly he moved his other foot. The ground felt springy now, but still firm enough to hold his weight. As long as I keep my face towards the breeze I should be all right, he thought.

The next minute he was sinking into the soft, wet fibrous mud.

Conn struggled frantically, but silently. He wouldn't risk anyone else's life because of his own stupidity, he vowed. Brian Boru had trusted him, and he had behaved like an impatient child.

He was deep in the mud, up to his knees now, but he was still able to do what he should have done at once. He threw himself backwards onto the bog, spreading his arms as wide as he could and praying that it would hold his weight.

His back and head remained above ground. That was more than he had dared to hope for. Now he had to gradually pull his legs clear. With all his strength, he tried to raise his right leg. It made a squelching sound, but he couldn't free it, and his efforts drove his back deeper into the soggy mess. He didn't dare try that again, or even his head would soon be under the bog. At the thought of the slow death by suffocation which awaited him, he sucked in his breath in a suppressed sob of agony.

It was then, when he had ceased to hope, that he heard a whisper. It was a strange voice, a strange accent. He hardly understood it at first.

'Say your name,' said the voice.

'Conn,' he whispered back.

1. To whose army did Conn belong?
2. What group was the army fighting?
3. Why were they fighting the Vikings?
4. When did the army hope to make the crossing?
5. Where had Conn led the army?
6. What was the danger of crossing this ground?
7. How did Conn try to stop himself from sinking?
8. Did Conn make the right choice in not telling the others that he was sinking? Explain your answer.

1. What words would you use to describe Conn's character? Give reasons for your answer.
2. Was the army wise to trust Conn's judgement? Explain your answer.
3. If you were Conn, what would you have done?
4. Do you think that the army will be successful in crossing without being caught?
5. In your opinion, who did the voice belong to?
6. Write five lines describing what you think will happen next.

Match the following words to their correct meaning:

• invade	showing care or warning in the face of danger
• hoard	an inborn power to respond to something in a certain way
• loot	to occupy in large numbers by force
• cautiously	hidden store of treasure
• instinct	goods stolen during a war or a riot
• squelching	to put an end to
• suffocation	acute physical or mental pain, anguish
• suppress	inability to breathe freely
• agony	walking with difficulty through soft, wet material or with wet shoes

Imagine that you are a member of Brian Boru's army. Give yourself a fictitious name.

You were part of the group crossing the bog with Brian Boru and Conn. Write a diary entry for that day.

Writing Accounts

We can use books and the Internet to find out about events that happened long ago. Read this account of 'The Golden Age' in Ireland.

'The Golden Age' in Ireland refers to the period 500–800 AD. During that time, many monasteries were built and began to flourish. Monks made chalices and crosses from gold and precious stones, which became valuable treasures. They produced beautiful manuscripts on vellum and parchment, such as The Book of Kells, which can be seen today in the library of Trinity College, Dublin. The monasteries also became great centres of learning, thus earning Ireland the title 'The Land of Saints and Scholars'.

Prior to writing this account, the writer would have asked a number of questions about 'The Golden Age'.

Write five questions that you think the writer would have asked.

Write an account about the Vikings. Use the Internet and/or books to research the Viking People. The following questions will guide you.

1 Who were the Vikings?
2 Where were they from?
3 When did they come to Ireland?
4 Why did they come to Ireland?
5 How did they travel to Ireland?
6 Where in Ireland did they settle?

Make up three more questions and include the answers in your account.

Nouns tell us the name of a person, place, animal or thing,
e.g. *Colin, Japan, horse, crayon.*

Rewrite the following sentences and underline the nouns.

Hint: Use your dictionary to help you!

1. Shane is going to China with his family next month.
2. The large elephant walked slowly around the jungle.
3. Daddy ate porridge and toast for his breakfast.
4. I travelled to Dublin by train on Saturday.
5. Our teacher told us about the sun, moon and stars in school today.
6. Gemma put her books, copies and lunch into her schoolbag.
7. I always put ham and pineapple on my pizzas.
8. The boy kicked his new football over the garden wall.

Fill in the gaps, using suitable nouns.

1. I ate a ____________ and a ____________ for lunch.
2. The capital city of ____________ is ____________.
3. I lost my pet ____________ in the ____________.
4. My friend ____________ bought new ____________ in the ____________.
5. The zookeeper fed the ____________, ____________ and ____________.
6. At night I can see the ____________ and lots of ____________ in the sky.
7. I got a ____________ and a ____________ for my birthday.
8. The little ____________ is wearing a new ____________.

Draw this table in your copy, filling in as many nouns as you can. Try different letters of the alphabet.

Letter	Boy's name	Girl's name	Place	Animal	Clothing/ Jewellery	Food/ Drink
A	Adam	Alison	America	ape	apron	apple
B	Barry	Barbara	Britain			
C	Colin	Carol				
D	David					
E						

Giving a Presentation

Giving a report or a presentation to an audience is common practice in schools, in colleges and in many jobs.

To be successful, the presenters need to prepare beforehand. They need to research their topic thoroughly, decide which points they are going to discuss and decide how they are going to present their work.

Choose a topic that you would like to present to your class.

Examples:
- your favourite sport
- an interesting book that you read or a film that you have seen
- an interesting place that you have visited
- your favourite person.

Use the K.W.L. chart to help you with your research.

K.W.L.

What I know	What I want to know	What I learned

Think about where you are going to find your information, e.g. books, magazines, interviews, the Internet.

How are you going to present your chosen topic to your audience?

You might:
- Read your information aloud
- Use an overhead projector
- Use photographs/posters/handouts
- Use a PowerPoint presentation

Here are some tips for the presentation!

- Stand on one spot in front of your audience or move around a little if you are comfortable with it.
- Look at your audience or glance frequently.
- Speak loudly.
- Speak clearly.
- Good luck!

Brain Teaser Make a list of words that you could use instead of the word 'big'.

- The letters **ph** make the sound **f**, e.g. ele**ph**ant

photo	phone	dolphin	orphan	nephew	graph
Stephanie	Ralph	Joseph	Philip	Phyllis	Philomena
phase	phrase	sphere	alphabet	triumph	geography
pheasant	physical	pharmacy	autograph	atmosphere	microphone

A Fill in the correct word. Use words from the wordbank above.

1. There are twenty-six letters in the ______________.
2. A ball is shaped like a ______________.
3. Dad went to the ______________ for the medicine.
4. A ______________ lives in the sea.
5. The children were tired after the ______________ activity.
6. Sarah asked the football star for his ______________.
7. The information was shown on a ______________.
8. Mark was nervous about speaking into the ______________.
9. ______________ is one of the subjects of SESE.
10. The ______________ spent the weekend at his aunt's house.

B Fill in the missing letters – f or ph. Use your dictionary to help you.

trium ___	___ orge	tele ___ one
___ oreign	paragra ___	beauti ___ ul
___ otogra ___	___ lood	___ oolish
___ orest	em ___ asis	___ ew!
___ ortnight	___ licker	___ ootball
___ araoh	___ riend	___ otocopy

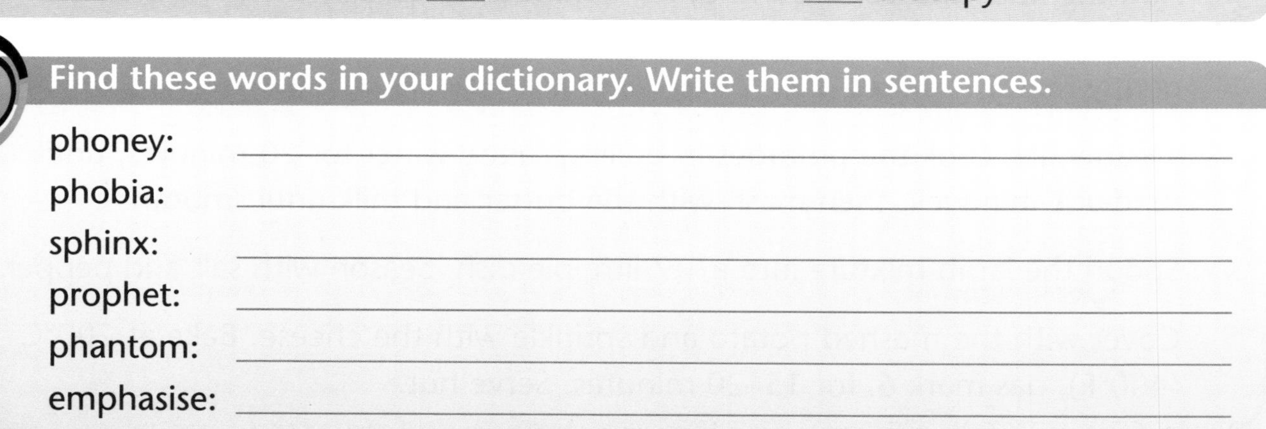

C Find these words in your dictionary. Write them in sentences.

phoney: ______________________________

phobia: ______________________________

sphinx: ______________________________

prophet: ______________________________

phantom: ______________________________

emphasise: ______________________________

Recipe: Shepherd's Pie

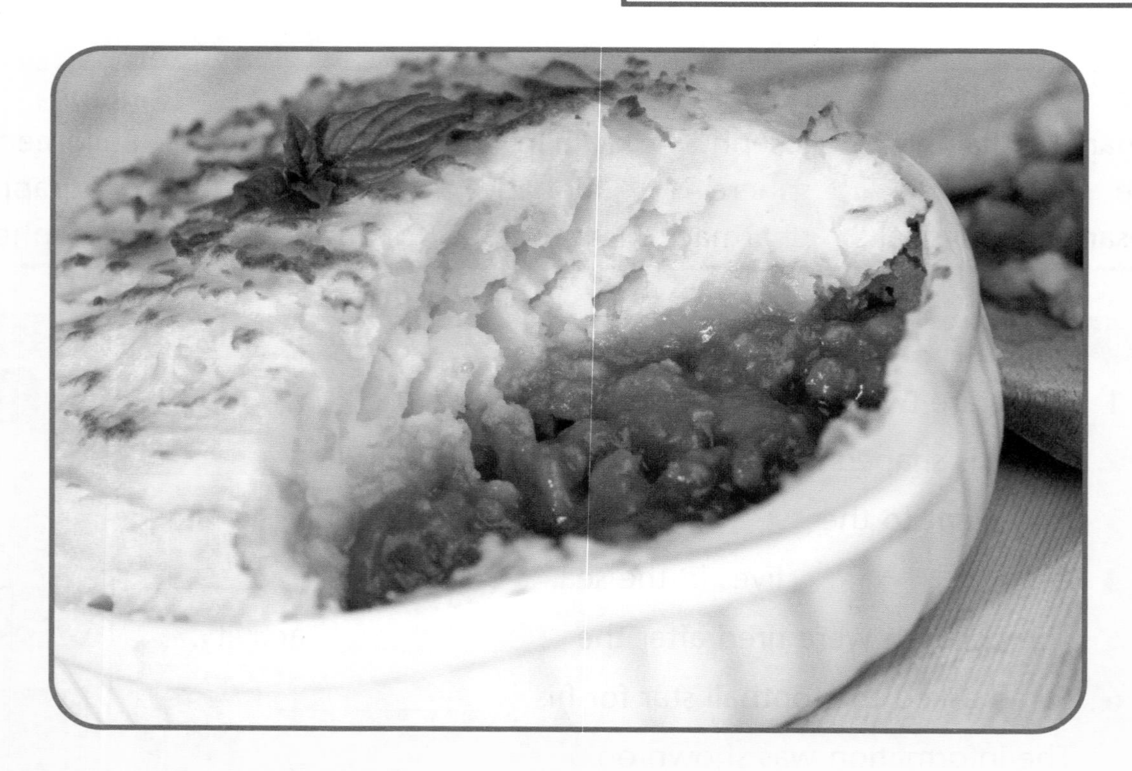

Ingredients:

- 1 large onion, peeled
- 50g mushrooms
- 2 carrots, peeled
- 450g lean minced lamb
- 30ml (2 tbsp) plain flour
- 300ml lamb stock
- 15ml (1 tbsp) tomato purée
- 700g potatoes, peeled and chopped
- salt and pepper
- 25g butter
- 60ml milk
- 50g Cheddar cheese

1. Chop the onion; slice the mushrooms and carrots. Fry the lamb in a non-stick frying pan with the onion, mushrooms and carrots for 8–10 minutes, stirring frequently.
2. Add the flour and cook, stirring, for 1 minute. Gradually blend in the stock and the tomato purée. Cook, stirring, until thickened. Cover and simmer gently for 25 minutes.
3. Meanwhile, cook the potatoes in boiling salted water for 20 minutes, until tender. Drain well, then mash with the butter and milk until smooth.
4. Spoon the lamb mixture into a 1.7 litre pie dish. Season with salt and pepper.
5. Cover with the mashed potato and sprinkle with the cheese. Bake at 200°C (400°F), gas mark 6, for 15–20 minutes. Serve hot.

1 What is the title of the recipe?
2 When might you eat this dish?
3 Which ingredients, do you think, are the main ingredients?
4 List all the ingredients that are vegetables.
5 Name the nearest shop to your house where you could buy (a) the vegetables and (b) the meat.
6 What cooking utensils are needed for this recipe?
7 How long altogether would it take to make the Shepherd's Pie?

1 List all the verbs in the recipe.
2 Can you substitute any of the following verbs with different action words/phrases while keeping the same meaning?

- chop
- fry
- add
- blend
- mash
- spoon
- simmer
- season
- sprinkle

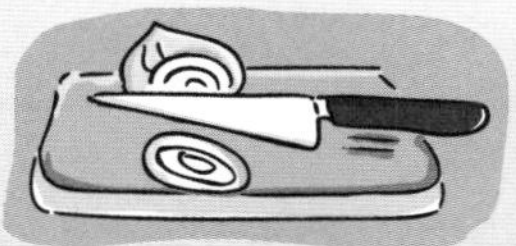

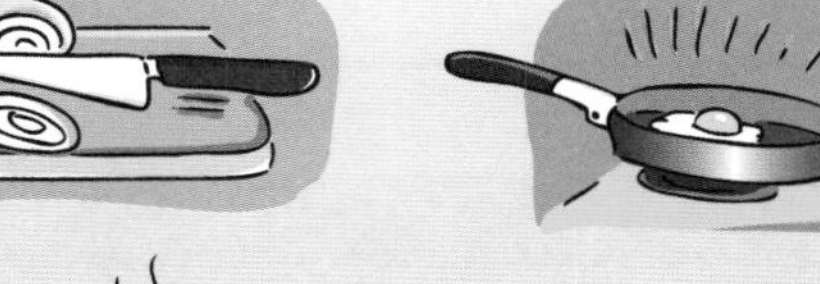

What is your favourite dinner recipe?

Find out how to make it and write it down. Do not forget the title, the ingredients and the steps of how to make it. Try to use as many of the verbs in B as you can. Illustrate your recipe.

Extension Work

Do you know the names of any famous chefs? Choose one and find out about him/her. Write his/her profile.

Restaurant Review: Gordon Ramsay

Based on an article by Aingeala Flannery

Friday 26 October 2007 – *The Independent*

Getting your foot in the door at the new Gordon Ramsay restaurant is no mean feat. It took five phone calls to finalise my reservation. Seafood features high on the menu, which offers plenty of choices including signature Ramsay dishes like lobster ravioli and John Dory with crushed potatoes. Luxurious and rich, the ravioli was perfectly balanced by a delicate yet zesty lemongrass and coriander sauce. Poached egg with crispy pancetta was smothered with vibrant spinach sauce, and was excellent. At no point did the cooking or the service falter. Main courses were assertive and delicious. The signature John Dory was fried golden; inside the flesh was immaculate and moist. The crushed new potatoes and tomatoes were lovingly prepared. The fillet of beef – perfectly cooked – was served with mashed yam and roasted peanuts. Restaurant Gordon Ramsay has hit the ground running. Everything was beyond criticism.

1. What words does the author use to describe:
   - the ravioli?
   - the main courses?
   - the John Dory?
   - the fillet of beef?
2. What adjectives does the author use for the:
   - lemongrass?
   - pancetta?
   - potatoes?
3. Write three things about the restaurant that the author praises.
4. Write one thing that the author criticises.

Write a review of a meal that you had.

- Were you in a restaurant, hotel or someone's house?
- Was the venue comfortable, clean, nicely decorated, dark, cluttered?
- How was the service?
- What did you order?
- Was the food tasty, well presented, cold, unpleasant?
- Would you return to the venue again?
- Use as many adjectives as you can in your review.

Verbs tell us about an action. They tell us what is happening.

Every sentence must have a **verb**, e.g.
The woman *drank* a cup of coffee.
We all *laughed* at the joke.

Rewrite the following sentences and underline the verbs.

1 The thief robbed the bank but was captured by the Gardaí.
2 Katy was chasing her friend when she fell and broke her leg.
3 The baby threw his dinner on the floor and started to cry.
4 The driver pressed the brakes when the lights turned red.
5 Jenny yawned as she climbed into bed and went to sleep.
6 The fireman rescued the woman from the burning building.
7 Keith won the lottery and bought a gorgeous new car.
8 I want to travel the world when I grow up.

Fill in the gaps, using the most suitable verb.

jumped ate went considered showed asked listened
won galloped tidied help send see wash

1 Laura ____________ her room on Saturday.
2 I _________ to the cinema with my friends to _________ the new film.
3 The horse ____________ over the fence and ____________ towards the finish line.
4 The teacher ____________ the class how to ____________ an email.
5 Dad ____________ me to ____________ him ____________ the car.
6 I ____________ to the radio as I ____________ my breakfast.
7 Sarah ________ a new bicycle in the raffle.
8 Mum _________________ buying a new television.

Read the clues and name the verb. (Answers on page 97.)

1 to join together c ______________
2 to leave behind a ______________
3 to make a choice d ______________
4 to draw i ______________
5 to fix or mend r ______________
6 to buy p ______________
7 to find l ______________
8 to say or do again r ______________

Social Situations

Every day, we react to different situations with different emotions. For example, when we meet our friends we are happy, if we win a prize we are excited, if we hear bad news we are shocked and saddened, if we do our best we are proud. It is very important to realise that while our reactions and emotions are natural, we must be careful not to hurt the feelings of others and we must behave in a dignified and respectful manner.

Read the following scenarios. In groups of three or four, decide how best to solve each situation. Groups take turns to dramatise each scenario. You may seek help from your teacher.

You and your friends have won first prize in a project competition. You are very proud of yourselves and very excited. Decide how you will inform the principal of your exciting win, describing the project, the competition, the prize and the prize-giving ceremony.

You and your family are at a restaurant to celebrate a special occasion. There is a delay with the order. When the meal finally arrives, the order is mixed up and the food is cold. Decide how you will make a complaint.

It is Saturday. You and your friends have decided to go to the cinema. On the way in, you notice another friend who also sees you. You feel bad because you forgot to invite him/her along and he/she is alone. What will you say to your friend?

You and your brother have just received a present of a computer game from your aunt and uncle. They went to a great deal of trouble to get it and they are very excited to see you open it. However, you have the game already! How do you react when they give it to you?

Brain Teaser Make a list of **fifteen** words that contain the letters 'ee'.

- Ch makes a '**ch**' sound, e.g. **ch**air.
- Ch makes a '**k**' sound, e.g. an**ch**or.
- Ch makes a '**sh**' sound, e.g. **ch**ampagne.

 **ch**air  an**ch**or  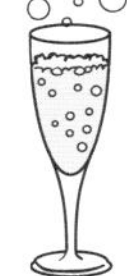 **ch**ampagne

Read the words. Write them in the correct place.

chimney	machine	choir	stomach	crochet	ache
batch	hutch	mechanic	echo	chisel	brochure
parachute	Christmas	teacher	stretch	chemist	chateau
chauffeur	orchestra	children	moustache	chestnut	chef

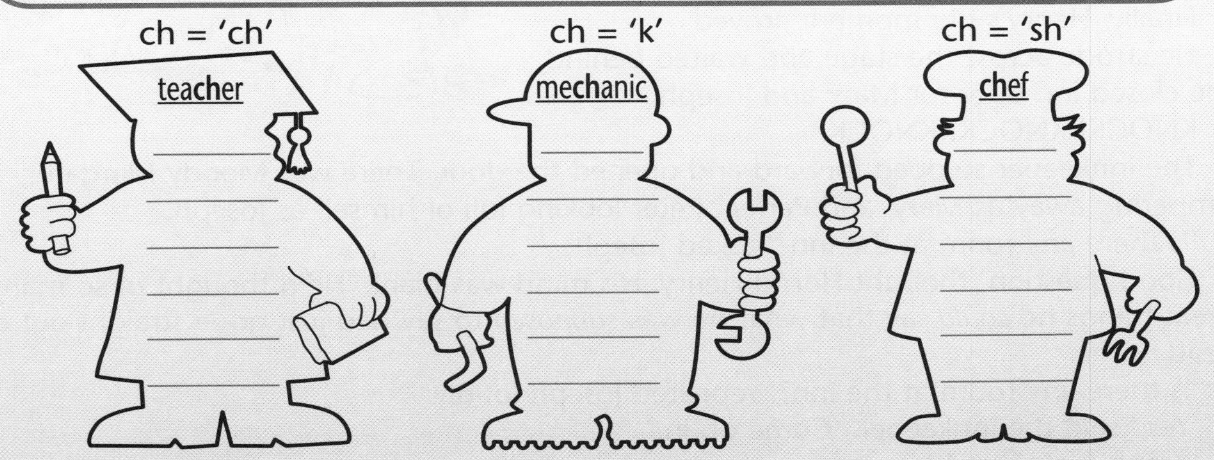

Read the meaning of the word. Write the word from the wordbank above.

1 A group of singers = ____________________
2 Unshaved hair above a man's upper lip = ____________________
3 A tool used by a carpenter = ____________________
4 A person employed to drive a car = ____________________
5 Knitting done with a one-hooked needle = ____________________
6 A French castle or country house = ____________________

Find these words in your dictionary. Write them in sentences.

architect: ____________________
chronic: ____________________
chaos: ____________________
scheme: ____________________
scholar: ____________________
schooner: ____________________

Horrid Henry's Christmas Play

22 December (only three more days till Christmas!)

Extract from Horrid Henry's Christmas Cracker *by Francesca Simon*

The big night had arrived. Horrid Henry was to play the part of the innkeeper.

Miss Battle-Axe started the CD player. The music pealed. The curtain rose. The audience stamped and cheered. Stars twinkled. Cows mooed. Horses neighed. Sheep baa'ed. Cameras flashed.

Horrid Henry stood in the wings and watched the shepherds do their Highland dance. He still hadn't decided for sure how he was going to play his part. There were so many possibilities. It was hard to choose.

Finally, Henry's big moment arrived.

He strode across the stage and waited behind the closed inn door for Mary and Joseph.

KNOCK! KNOCK! KNOCK!

The innkeeper stepped forward and opened the door. There was Moody Margaret, simpering away as Mary, and Perfect Peter looking full of himself as Joseph.

'Is there any room at the inn?' asked Joseph.

Good question, thought Horrid Henry. His mind was blank. He'd thought of so many great things he *could* say that what he was *supposed* to say had just gone straight out of his head.

'Is there any room at the inn?' repeated Joseph loudly.

'Yes,' said the innkeeper. 'Come on in.'

Joseph looked at Mary.

Mary looked at Joseph.

The audience murmured.

Oops, thought Horrid Henry. Now he remembered. He'd been supposed to say no. Oh well, in for a penny, in for a pound.

The innkeeper grabbed Mary and Joseph's sleeves and yanked them through the door. 'Come on in, I haven't got all day.'

'....but....but...the inn's *full*,' said Mary.

'No, it isn't,' said the innkeeper.

'Is too.'

'Is not. It's my inn and I should know. This is the best inn in Bethlehem, we've got TVs and beds, and —' the innkeeper paused for a moment. What *did* inns have in them? '— and computers!'

Mary glared at the innkeeper.

The innkeeper glared at Mary.

Miss Battle-Axe gestured frantically from the wings.

'This inn looks full to me,' said Mary firmly. 'Come on, Joseph, let's go to the stable.'

'Oh, don't go there; you'll get fleas,' said the innkeeper.

'So?' said Mary.

'I love fleas,' said Joseph weakly.

'And it's full of manure.'

'So are you,' snapped Mary.

'Don't be horrid, Mary,' said the innkeeper severely. 'Now sit down and rest your weary bones and I'll sing you a song.' And the innkeeper started singing:

'Ten green bottles, standing on a wall …'

'OOOHHH!' moaned Mary. 'I'm having the baby.'

'Can't you wait till I've finished my song?' snapped the innkeeper.

'NO!' bellowed Mary …

Miss Battle-Axe ran on stage and nabbed him.

'Thank you, innkeeper. Your other guests need you now,' said Miss Battle-Axe, grabbing him by the collar.

'Merry Christmas!' shrieked Horrid Henry as she yanked him off-stage.

1 What part did Horrid Henry have in the play?
2 What was the teacher's name?
3 Describe the opening scene when the curtain was raised.
4 What kind of dance did the shepherds do?
5 Who played the parts of Mary and Joseph?
6 What song did the innkeeper sing?
7 What were Horrid Henry's parting words?

1 Was Henry happy with the part he had in the play? Give reasons for your answer.
2 Do you think that 'Mary' and 'Joseph' played their parts well when Horrid Henry said the wrong lines?
3 In your opinion, how did Miss Battle-Axe feel as she watched from the wings?
4 Does Miss Battle-Axe's name suit her character? Give reasons for your answer.
5 Would you have enjoyed the play if you were part of the audience? Explain your answer.
6 How, do you think, did Horrid Henry's parents feel as they watched their son on the stage?
7 What words would you use to describe Horrid Henry's character?

Write the meanings of the following words. Use your dictionary.

peal simper murmur glare frantic bellow

In the story, there is a saying: 'In for a penny, in for a pound'.

Find out what this saying means and write it down. Do you know any more sayings? Ask an older person if he/she knows any old sayings. Write the sayings and their meanings in your copy.

Creative Ideas

Art Books

We can get lots of creative ideas from art books. Art books give lists of materials needed to create pieces of art, as well as step-by-step instructions. Often they contain pictures or photographs that can help to show what needs to be done.

Alternative Christmas Tree

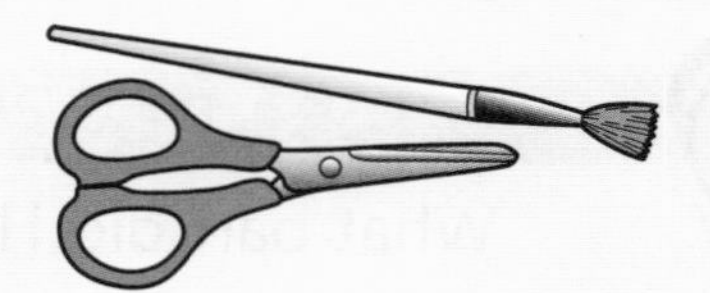

Things you need:

- *old branch*
- *old wrapping paper*
- *empty matchboxes*
- *scissors*
- *white paint*
- *sticky tape*
- *coloured paper*
- *cotton wool*
- *paint brush*
- *foil plates*
- *string or ribbon*
- *stones and sand*

1. Paint an old branch with white paint and leave to dry.
2. Decorate a bucket using used wrapping paper, and fill with sand.
3. Wrap old matchboxes with coloured paper as if they were presents.
4. Tie some string or ribbons around the boxes and hang on the tree.
5. Twist some foil plates into spirals to make them look like icicles.
6. Make a small hole on one end. Thread some string through so you can hang them on the tree.
7. Stand the branch in the sand. Cover the sand with stones and add some cotton wool to give a snowy effect.

Answer these questions:

(a) What is the title of this activity?
(b) List five items needed to do this activity.
(c) How many steps or instructions are in the activity?

Choose a science or an art activity that you completed and would like to share with your friend.

1. Name the activity.
2. Write the list of materials needed.
3. Write the steps or instructions.
4. Illustrate the activity.

Something that is happening now is in the **present tense**.

Something that has already happened is in the **past tense**.

Something that will happen is in the **future tense**.

Verbs can have different endings to let us know if something happens in the present, happened in the past or will happen in the future,

e.g.	**Present**	**Past**	**Future**
	walk	*walked*	*will walk*
	jog	*jogged*	*will jog*
	dry	*dried*	*will dry*

A Draw the table in your copy and fill in the gaps.

Present Tense	Past Tense	Future Tense
________	talked	________
jump	________	________
________	________	will wash
________	hoped	________
________	________	will skip
hop	________	________
________	cried	________
________	________	will use

B Write these sentences, putting the verb into the correct tense.

1 Sam (watch) __________ a film on the television last night.
2 Jenny (play) _______ _______ football with her friends next Sunday.
3 We all (smile) __________ in the photograph.
4 I (carry) __________ the heavy box up to my bedroom yesterday.
5 Mammy has promised that she (bake) ________ ________ a cake tomorrow.
6 Dad (slip) __________ on the ice this morning.
7 Karen (tidy) __________ her bedroom last Saturday.
8 The two girls (dance) ______ ______ to the music later.

Unit 8 Dictionary Skills (1)

Word Hunt

In your dictionary, find four examples of each of the following and write their meanings:

1 words beginning with 'que'
2 words ending with 'ge'
3 words beginning with 'x'
4 words ending with 'sh'
5 words beginning with 'ch'
6 words ending with 'tion'

Context Clues

Read the following sentences. Choose the word most similar in meaning to the underlined words.

1 The judge of the talent show was happy with the calibre of the contestants.
(a) songs (b) age (c) quality (d) size

2 The tide began to ebb.
(a) flow back (b) rise (c) splash (d) become deep

3 The expensive vase had a hallmark on its base.
(a) crack (b) scratch (c) stain (d) symbol

4 The president praised the soldier's integrity.
(a) uniform (b) honour (c) happiness (d) army tank

5 The mistake on the poster was blatant.
(a) big (b) obvious (c) small (d) noticeable

6 The dubious character crept silently along the dark street.
(a) ugly (b) doubtful (c) suspicious (d) tall

- What is the first word in your dictionary?
- What is the last word in your dictionary?
- Put each word into a sentence of its own.

Fact or Fib?

Choose an unusual word from the dictionary. Write the true definition and two other definitions that are untrue. Call out the word and the three definitions to your class. Try to be convincing. Your classmates must decide which definition is fact or fib.

Remember the 'ik' rule? (Page 17)

Fill in the word wheels with words that end in an 'ik' sound.

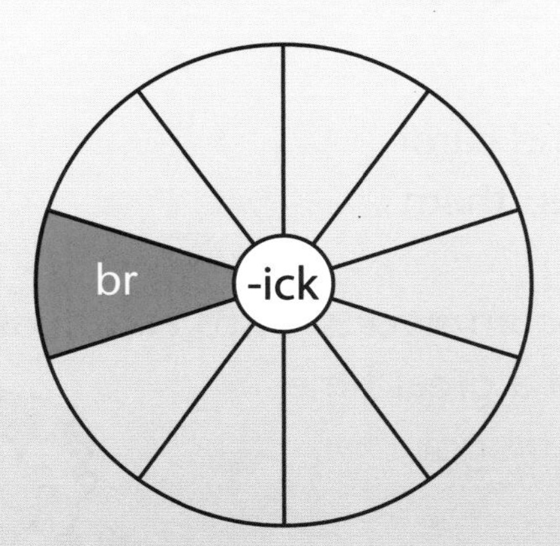

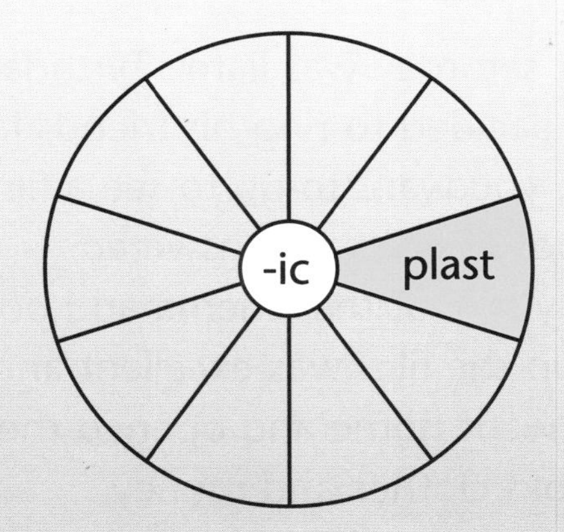

Circle the correct spelling: -ar, -er, -or.

lettar	dollar	mayar	feathar
letter	doller	mayer	feather
lettor	dollor	mayor	feathor

Rewrite the following paragraph.

Highlight the words where n and gh are silent. (13 in total)

Last autumn we went on holidays to Brighton with our neighbours. During the flight our neighbour's eight-year-old daughter, Emma, was very naughty. She threw a tantrum which seemed to last forever. We thought it would never end. Her mother was distraught.

Finally, the steward spoke to Emma in a solemn tone.

'No more of this nonsense on this plane,' he warned.

To everybody's delight, that was the end of naughty Emma's tantrum. Until the next time!

A Rewrite the sentences, using the correct punctuation.

18 Capital letters 12 Full stops 3 Question marks 4 Commas

last saturday was liam's birthday
he decided to ring his friends jack fred and carol
'do you want to go to see a film' he asked them
'good idea,' they answered
they met at the cinema and bought popcorn sweets crisps and drinks at the shop the film was excellent and they had a great time
he went home and opened the presents he got
books clothes and money
'do you want your last present' asked mam
'what is it' he wondered
it was a puppy he was delighted

B Put the words in alphabetical order.

1 blue blood blessing blister blanket
2 dream drawer drum drill dryer
3 slice sling slime slide sleeve
4 crocodile crisp crumb crow cream

C Write 'noun' or 'verb' beside the correct words.

hospital	________	baby	________
skipping	________	mouse	________
France	________	go	________
drank	________	blanket	________
skirt	________	jumped	________
Gemma	________	chair	________

D Write these sentences correctly.

1 Jim (wash) ________ his car yesterday.
2 Sam (hit) ________ the ball with a racket.
3 Mary (hope) ________ that she would win the competition.
4 The little girl (cry) ________ when she fell.
5 I (walk) ________ ________ to town tomorrow.
6 The man (rub) ________ his hands together to keep warm.

The Skeleton

important	protect	skull	heap	sizes	arm
tube	skeleton	bend	muscles	stiff	
vertebrae	spine	straight	attached	separate	

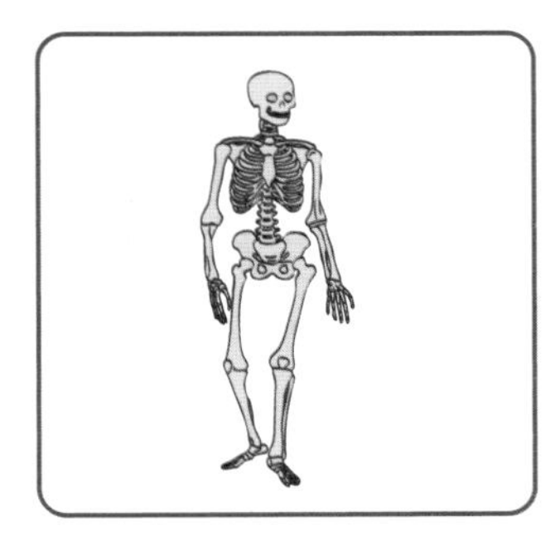
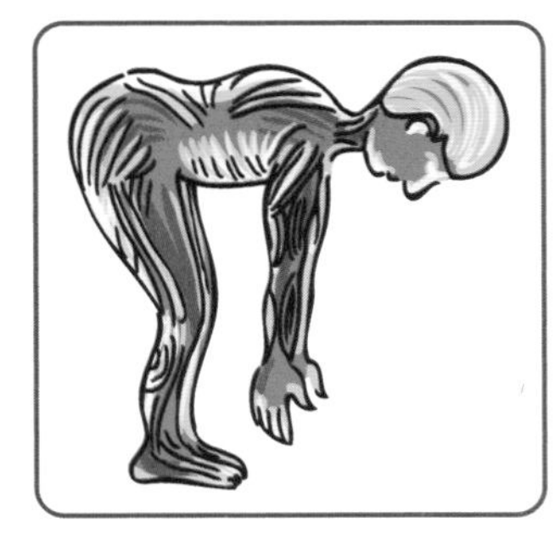

You have 206 bones in your body – bones of different shapes and ____________. These bones are all joined together to form your ______________.

Bones are hard and ______________. They help ______________ your heart and lungs and brain and other parts of your body.

Muscles are ______________ to your bones. Whenever you want to walk, or even scratch your head, your ______________ pull on your bones to move just the right part of your body – a finger, a toe, an ______________, a foot.

The thirty-three bones in your backbone, or ______________, are the most ______________ bones in your body. These bones are ______________, yet they are joined together by muscles to form a long, bony ______________ from the base of your ______________ down to your lower back. These bones, or ______________, as they are called, help you to stand up ______________, but they also allow you to move easily and to ______________.

Without your backbone, you would fall over in a ______________!

Giving Directions

Left

Right

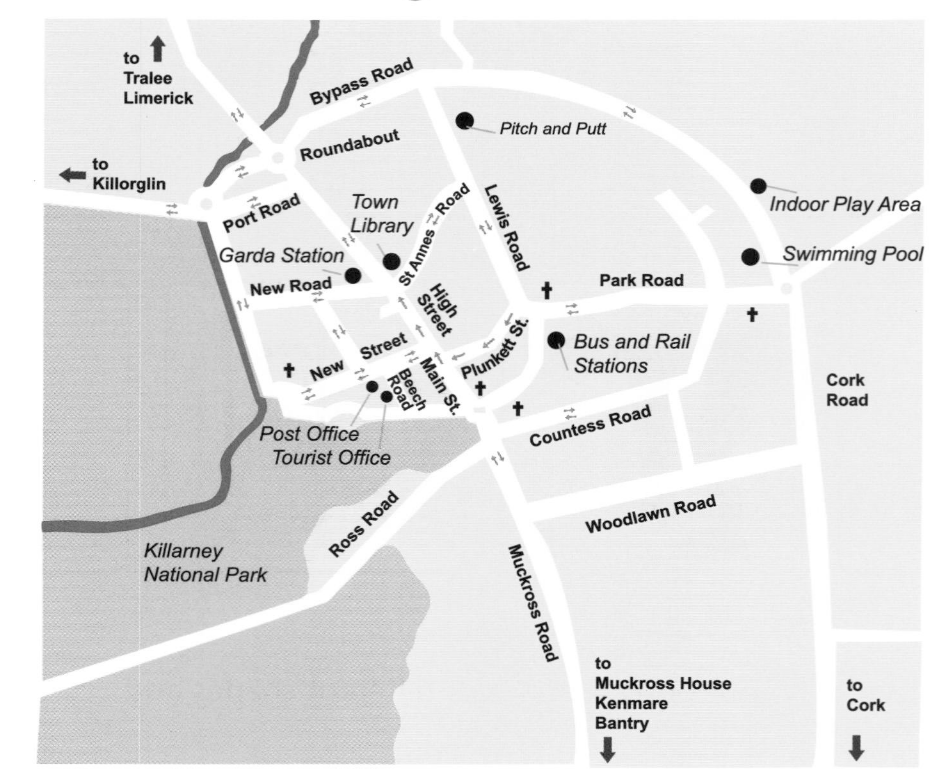

Roundabout

Continue straight ahead

1 Which streets are for: (a) one-way traffic only? (b) two-way traffic?

2 Work out which road or street you will be on if you follow these directions:

(a) You are standing at the Post Office on New Street. Turn right. Take the first right.

(b) You are standing outside the tourist office. Walk along Beech Road to New Street. Turn right. Continue straight ahead. Turn left.

(c) You are at the library. Turn right. Walk up the road until you come to a roundabout. Take the third exit.

1 Ellen is standing outside the Bus Station.
What directions would you give her to walk to:
(a) the Pitch and Putt? (b) the Library? (c) the Swimming Pool?

2 Ben is parked outside the Garda Station. What directions would you give him to drive to:
(a) the Railway Station? (b) the Indoor Play Area? (c) the Cork Road?

3 Choose a starting point on the map. Select five different places. Give your friend the directions to get from the starting point to each of the five places. Your friend must guess each of the destinations.

Brain Teaser Make a list of words that end with 'ch'.

- The letters **u** and **ue** are usually silent when they come after **g**, e.g. g**u**ard.

Read the clues. Fill in the missing letters.

1 a musical instrument with six strings — g _ _ _ _ _
2 a place where dead bodies are laid — _ _ _ g _ _
3 a mischievous person, a rascal — _ _ g _ _
4 an association of clubs for games — _ _ _ g _ _
5 another word for a visitor — g _ _ _ _
6 to lead or show the way — g _ _ _ _
7 blamed for breaking the law — g _ _ _ _ _
8 used for executing by beheading — g _ _ _ _ _ _ _ _ _

- The letter **v** at the end of a word is always followed by a silent **e**, e.g. do**ve**.

Read the clues. Fill in the missing letters.

1 opposite of below — _ _ _ v _
2 used to keep hands warm — _ _ _ v _ _
3 cut up (meat) into slices — _ _ _ v _
4 suffer greatly from hunger — _ _ _ _ v _
5 place where a dead person is buried — _ _ _ v _
6 someone forced to work for a master — _ _ _ v _
7 a small group of trees — _ _ _ v _
8 turn a car quickly to one side — _ _ _ _ v _

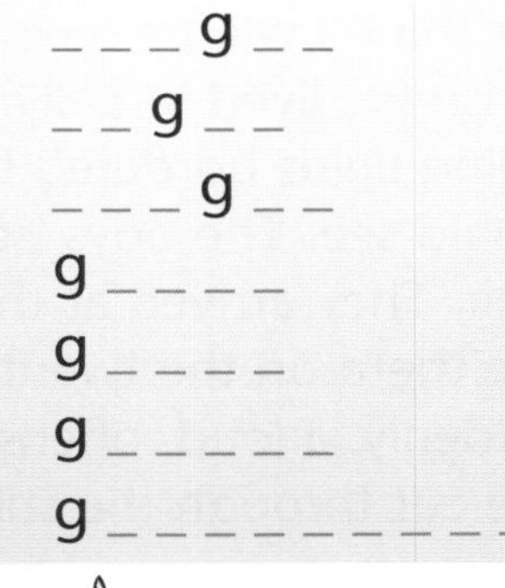

- Usually **i** comes before **e** except after **c**, e.g. th**ie**f, rec**ei**pt.

Read the clues. Fill in the missing letters.

1 a part of something — p _ _ _ _
2 to trust in something or someone — b _ _ _ _ _ _
3 have something given to you — r _ _ _ _ _ _
4 a buddy, chum or mate — f _ _ _ _ _
5 to tell lies or mislead — d _ _ _ _ _ _
6 deep sorrow (after a death) — g _ _ _ _
7 the head of a clan or tribe — c _ _ _ _ _ _ _ _ _
8 a sales slip, proof of purchase — r _ _ _ _ _ _

The Happening Place

One frosty, Monday morning in January, Chris and Andy slowly made their way to the bus stop.

'The other kids will have exciting stories about what they did over the weekend,' said Andy miserably.

'Nothing ever happens around here,' replied Chris. 'The most exciting event lately was when Farmer Con's gaggle of geese ended up as the main course at a fox's dinner party! I don't think I will be telling *that* to the gang at break time.'

'I wish we lived in Ballyowen and not here in the middle of nowhere.'

Rolling fields bordered by wild bushes tinged with frost surrounded them as far as the eye could see. The boys both sighed and watched as their breaths billowed into the cold, crisp air. They arrived at the bus stop with ten minutes to spare before the school bus came to take them on the twenty-minute journey to Ballyowen National School.

Suddenly, a loud, offensive sound of an engine cut through the stillness of the countryside.

'The bus is early,' tutted Andy.

'That's no bus!' exclaimed Chris slowly. 'That, my man, is a limo!'

Both lads stood in astonishment, with jaws hanging in mid-air, as the shiny, blacked-out limousine ground to a halt before them.

An electric window opened smoothly to reveal a large, muscular chauffeur wearing sun-glasses and a black over-coat.

'Good morning, guys. I think we are a little lost. Could you point us in the direction of Ballyowen, please?' he asked in a strong American accent.

Andy and Chris looked at each other in amazement before returning their gaze to the limousine and its stern driver.

'I take it that you guys don't know the way to Ballyowen?' asked the driver with eyebrows raised.

'Oh, we do, we do!' stuttered Chris. 'Sorry. We usually don't see cars like yours around here, that's all.'

Just as Chris finished speaking, another electric window to the rear of the car opened to reveal more occupants.

'I've got to be seeing things!' screamed Chris, jumping up and down ecstatically.

'And I've got to be dreaming,' whispered Andy in a trance.

Before their very eyes, on a narrow country road in rural Ireland, sat the latest rock sensations to hit the international charts in the last year.

'Hi guys! What are ye up to?' asked the lead singer and guitarist.

'We are waiting for the school bus,' Andy replied shakily.

The drummer sat forward and said, 'We are on our way to Ballyowen for a photo-shoot for our next album. Which way is it?'

'Take the next left, then right and continue til you come to crossroads. Turn left and the road will take you straight to Ballyowen,' answered Chris confidently, after regaining his composure.

'Thanks, guys! You want some tickets to our gig?'

'Absolutely!' said Andy without hesitation.

'Thank you so much!' called Chris.

The two boys peered at the tickets as the electric windows closed and the limousine slowly moved away.

'Two tickets to see the band in the O2 Arena in May! Wait until everyone at school hears about this,' laughed Andy. 'This place isn't so bad after all!'

1. What were Chris and Andy complaining about?
2. What were the boys surprised to see instead of the school bus?
3. Where was the chauffeur from?
4. Who were the occupants of the limousine?
5. Why did the band want to go to Ballyowen?
6. What gift did the band give to the boys?
7. Where and when will the band play their concert?
8. Why were the boys looking forward to going to school?

1. Did the boys like living where they did? How do you know?
2. What 'exciting' incident happened in their locality recently?
3. How do you know that the boys were awestruck to see the limousine and its occupants?
4. Do you think the boys' classmates will believe them when they tell them what happened on their way to school?
5. If you won free tickets to a concert of your choice, who would you go to see and why?
6. Imagine that you meet a celebrity by chance. Write a paragraph, describing the event.

Dictionary Work

Use your dictionary to look up the meaning of the following words from the story. Write a sentence using each word.

gaggle	tinge	billow	offensive
chauffeur	trance	international	composure

Terrible Tricks

Magic Envelope Trick

Trick

The magician asks a friend to write down four numbers on a piece of paper. Then he asks the friend to add up or total the numbers. The magician opens a sealed envelope and it has the same number as the friend's total!

Things you need:

- *a piece of paper*
- *a pen*
- *an envelope*

Secret

1. Before the show, write down a four-figure number that is twice the current year's date. In the year 2010, the number would be 4020; in the year 2011, the number would be 4022; and so on.
2. Seal the paper in the envelope.
3. Ask your friend to write down the year that he/she was born.
4. Ask your friend to write down the year of an important date in his/her life, for example, the year that he/she started school.
5. Ask your friend to write down the age that he/she will turn this current year.
6. Ask your friend to write down the number of years that have passed since the important event. (This must be a whole number.)
7. Ask your friend to add up the four numbers.
8. Open the envelope. Your friend's total will be the same as the number you already wrote down!

Try this trick on family members and friends!

Have you ever played a trick on someone? Write a description of the trick.

- What was the trick?
- Who was the 'victim'?
- Why did you decide to play the trick?
- Where did it take place?
- When did it take place?
- What happened?

Adjectives are describing words. They tell us more about nouns.
Examples:
The *stern* teacher was cross with the *naughty* boy.
The *beautiful*, *black* horse raced around the *green* field.

Rewrite the following sentences and underline the adjectives.

1 The tall, slim lady crossed the busy street.
2 The large, vicious dog chased the terrified girl.
3 The young lady brushed her long, straight, shiny hair.
4 Lucy wrapped a warm, red coat around her shivering body.
5 The exhausted boy rested in the comfortable chair.
6 I watched as the little baby threw his soft teddy onto the floor.
7 *The Hulk* is a good film about a scary, green monster.
8 We drove to the quiet, sandy beach in our old, blue car.

B Make these sentences more interesting by adding adjectives.

1 The ____________ boy played in the ____________ park.
2 The ____________ footballer kicked the ____________ ball.
3 Linda was wearing a ____________ and ____________ dress.
4 The ____________ nurse helped the ____________ man.
5 I ate the ____________ ice-cream.
6 A ____________ mouse ate the ____________ cheese.
7 The ____________ man climbed the ____________ mountain.
8 The ____________ principal spoke to the ____________ class.

To catch a thief

You have just witnessed a robbery and must give a detailed description of the thief to the Gardai.

Use adjectives to describe the thief's physical appearance and clothing.

He was ________________________.
His hair was ________________________.
He was wearing ________________________________.

Fun with Words (2)

Listening and Concentrating

Game: Find the missing one!

- Look at the list of words below. Call out five words.
- Call out the words again, leaving out the underlined word.
- Which word is missing?

(a)	comb	<u>shampoo</u>	clip	brush	slide
(b)	rabbit	puppy	mouse	<u>canary</u>	kitten
(c)	<u>ship</u>	yacht	ferry	canoe	boat
(d)	football	tennis	badminton	golf	<u>soccer</u>

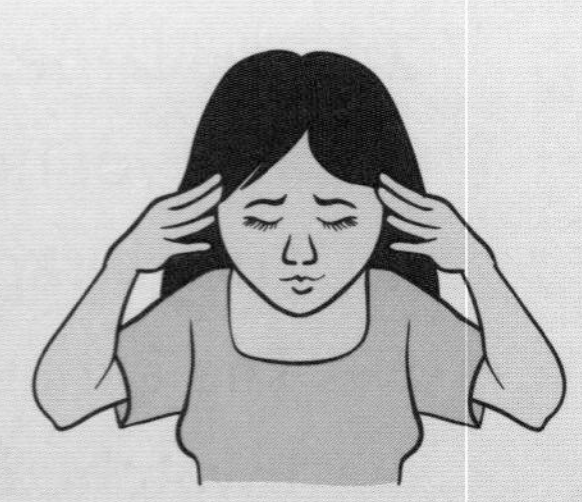

Now think of other sets of related words that you could use to play this game.

How you say it!

A sentence containing the same words may have different meanings, depending on the tone of voice used and the speed at which they are spoken. For example, say this sentence in the following ways:

(1) sadly (2) excitedly (3) angrily (4) lazily

'I want to go.'

What other tones of voice could you use?
Now try these sentences using different tones of voice.

- Thank you so much.
- She asked me to call her.
- Sorry I'm late.
- They will arrive tonight.

Linking Lists!

Choose a theme, e.g. food. One person thinks of any food, e.g. apple. The second person must name another food beginning with the last letter of appl**e**, e.g. egg. The third person must think of a food beginning with the last letter of eg**g**, e.g. grapes.

Here are some more themes to choose from:

- places
- girls' names
- boys' names
- famous people

Think of some more themes and try this game with your friends!

Brain Teaser Describe your favourite food in exactly **ten** words.

- Homophones are words that sound the same but have a different spelling and meaning, e.g. **There** was a big crowd at the game./I left my bag over **there**.
  We visited **their** house yesterday.
  They're as good as gold.

Fill in the correct word.

1 The children were thrilled when ___________ team won.
2 ___________ was a very bad thunder storm last night.
3 '___________ always ready to lend a hand,' said the proud teacher.
4 Very few tickets were sold for ___________ concert.
5 'Pay them what ___________ owed,' said the boss.
6 ___________ are twelve months in a year.
7 ___________ is a beautiful tree growing in ___________ garden.
8 ___________ usually at ___________ nana's house on Sunday.
9 ___________ too lazy to clean ___________ room.
10 On ___________ way to the airport ___________ was a bad accident.

Identify the correct word. Fill in the blanks.

bear/bare

beach/beech

seller/cellar

peace/piece

1 The ___________ roamed the forest in search of food.
2 A ___________ tree was planted near the entrance to the park.
3 The wine was stored in the ___________ of the large house.
4 The people hoped the ___________ talks would be a success.
5 I am reading a ___________ book at the moment.
6 The ___________ did not outsmart the tortoise in the story.
7 Sarah ___________ all the team members.
8 Tony froze when he heard the ___________ turning in the lock.

great/grate

hare/hair

nose/knows

key/quay

Find these words in your dictionary. Put eight of these words into sentences.

hole/whole	hail/hale	lair/layer	mare/mayor	pray/prey
mail/male	mussel/muscle	pain/pane	ring/wring	root/route

The Climb

Extract from Everest – The Climb *by Gordon Korman*

Dominic Alexis was waiting his turn to use the airplane bathroom when he got his first glimpse of Mount Everest.

Standing there in the narrow aisle of the 747, he froze, gawking out the porthole in the emergency door. To the north rose the jagged, icy spires of the Himalayas, the highest mountain range on the face of the earth. And right in the heart of it, the giant among giants – barely lower than the cruising altitude of the plane – Everest.

There should be trumpets, he thought reverently. *A fanfare. Fireworks.*

Norman 'Tilt' Crowley came up behind Dominic and hip-checked him out of the way.

'Man, this airline stinks! What do you have to do to get a bag of peanuts?'

Wordlessly, Dominic pointed out the window at the unmistakable silhouette.

Tilt peered through the porthole. 'Big deal – Mount Everest. What, you thought they were going to move it before we got here?'

But for all his attitude, Tilt stayed riveted to the spot, fascinated by the sight of the big mountain that the Nepalese called *Jongmalungma* – 'Goddess, Mother of the World'.

An announcement came from the cockpit. 'On our left, we see Mount Everest.' It was repeated in several other languages.

There was a rush for the left side of the plane. For most of the passengers, this was the closest they would come to the top of the world. But Dominic and Tilt were part of SummitQuest, the youngest expedition ever to attempt the planet's highest peak. For them, the massive profile of Everest was the shape of things to come.

Sammi Moon shut off her Walkman and rushed over to join them at the porthole.

'How is it? Extreme, right?' She spotted the mountain. 'It's beautiful!'

'You paint it; I'll climb it,' put in Tilt. 'That lump of rock is going to make me famous.'

'We have to wake Perry,' said Dominic. 'He should see this.'

The fourth member of their team, Perry Noonan, was in his seat, fast asleep.

'Are you kidding?' snorted Tilt. 'He's so scared of Everest that he can't even face the picture in the in-flight magazine. He'd take one look out the window and wet his pants!'

Dominic's eyes never left the mountain. 'You're crazy if you're not a little scared.'

'I'm just amped,' said Sammi. 'I can't believe we're really on our way!'

They squinted through the clouds, trying to discern the summit – the object of years of climbing and months of preparation.

What Dominic, Tilt, Sammi, and Perry could not know was that the mist-obscured peak was more than a goal. For one of the four team members, it would be a final resting place.

1. What type of airplane were the teenagers travelling on?
2. In what mountain range is Mount Everest?
3. What do the Nepalese call Mount Everest?
4. What was the name of the expedition that the teenagers were part of?
5. Name the teenagers that were part of the expedition.
6. What were the teenagers hoping to achieve?
7. Had the team done much preparation?
8. What is meant by 'it would be a final resting place'?

1. How, do you think, did Dominic feel when he saw Mount Everest?
2. Did Tilt hold the same feelings as Dominic? Why?/Why not?
3. In your opinion, which of the teenagers were looking forward to the climb and which were not?
4. List all the words/phrases that describe Mount Everest and the Himalayas.
5. 'For them the massive profile of Everest was the shape of things to come.' In your opinion, what does this sentence mean?
6. Write four sentences predicting what you think will happen next.

Dictionary Work

Use your dictionary/thesaurus to find the meanings of these words:

- glimpse
- altitude
- reverently
- fanfare
- silhouette
- fascinated
- profile
- discern
- summit
- obscured

Extension Work

Imagine that you are one of the teenagers taking part in the expedition. Write a diary entry while you are on the airplane. Outline how you are feeling about the trip and whether you are looking forward to it or not.

Biographies

A **biography** is the story of a person's life, written by another person.

Biographies often provide information about the family of the person and what happened to the person when he/she was growing up. It usually contains details about that person's achievements and disappointments, hopes and dreams. Many celebrities, including sports stars, politicians, movie stars and pop stars, have had biographies written about them.

Visit a local library or bookshop. Find the names of four biographies.

Pretend that you are writing the biography of a famous person. What would you include in it? Use the following factfile to help you:

Name:	
Lives in:	
Date of birth:	
Place of birth:	
Family:	
Occupation:	
Achievements:	
Interesting facts:	

Autobiographies

An autobiography is the story of a person's life, written by himself/herself.

If you were to write your own autobiography, what interesting facts/achievements would you include?

Choose one of these facts/achievements and write about it.

For example, winning a competition, or visiting an exciting place.

- What age were you?
- Where were you?
- Who was with you?
- What happened?
- How did you feel?
- How did the story end?

Adverbs tell us more about a verb.
Adverbs usually end in 'ly',
e.g. Jim smiled **happily** for the photograph.

A Change these adjectives into adverbs by adding 'ly'.

sad	=	sadly	loud	=	________
silent	=	________	bad	=	________
safe	=	________	proud	=	________
quick	=	________	brave	=	________
slow	=	________	careful	=	________

B Change these adjectives to adverbs. Drop the 'y' and add 'ily'.

hungry	=	hungrily	sleepy	=	________
happy	=	________	lazy	=	________
busy	=	________	angry	=	________
noisy	=	________	weary	=	________
clumsy	=	________	heavy	=	________

C Fill in the gaps, using suitable adverbs.

1 Steve ran ________ to school because he was late.
2 The children played ________ in the garden.
3 We waited ________ in the queue for the concert tickets.
4 The thief crept ________ around the house.
5 Dad waited ________ in the car while I got my coat.
6 I laughed ________ when I heard the joke.

D Match the adverb to the clue.

wisely casually politely cruelly
correctly silently calmly eventually

1 making no noise ________
2 finally ________
3 in a relaxed way ________
4 with manners ________
5 without getting excited ________
6 in a nasty way ________
7 being very clever ________
8 done the right way ________

Phone Calls

Using a phone is one of the most common forms of communication.
We use a phone to:

- chat to others
- find out information
- give information.

With a partner, practise making and receiving phone calls based on the following scenarios. Take turns at each role.

Scenario 1: Reserving tickets for a show

Child 1: Contact the 'Box Office' at the Concert Hall. Enquire as to what shows are on, who they are suitable for, times and prices of tickets.

Child 2: The person working at the Box Office. Give all the relevant information and make the reservations.

Scenario 2: Playing a request on a radio station

Child 1: Contact the local radio station. Enquire if it is possible to play a request for a friend's birthday. Give the name and age of your friend and when the birthday is to be celebrated.

Child 2: The person who takes the calls. Write down the request, including name, age and birthday. Ask what song the person would like to dedicate to his/her friend.

Scenario 3: Find out information about a summer camp

Child 1: You received a leaflet about an interesting summer camp that will take place in your area. Contact the organisers to find out what activities will be available, what dates they are on and the cost of the summer camp.

Child 2: You are the organiser of the summer camp. Give all the relevant information to the caller.

Scenario 4: Inform the local newspaper of an upcoming event in your school

Child 1: Contact the local newspaper about a concert that is to be held in your school in aid of charity. Give a list of the different acts that will be performing, the name of the charity that will benefit from the proceeds and when the concert will take place.

Child 2: Take down the relevant information. Find out when it is on and any other information.

Brain Teaser Make a list of foods that can be baked.

- One-syllable words that end in a **'j'** sound after a short vowel are spelled **-dge**, e.g. e**dge**.
- One-syllable words that end in a **'j'** sound after a long vowel are spelled **-ge**, e.g. ra**ge**.
- Words of more than one syllable that end in a **'j'** sound are usually spelled **age**, e.g. vill**age**.

A Say the word. Fill in the missing letters.

-ge **-dge** **-age**

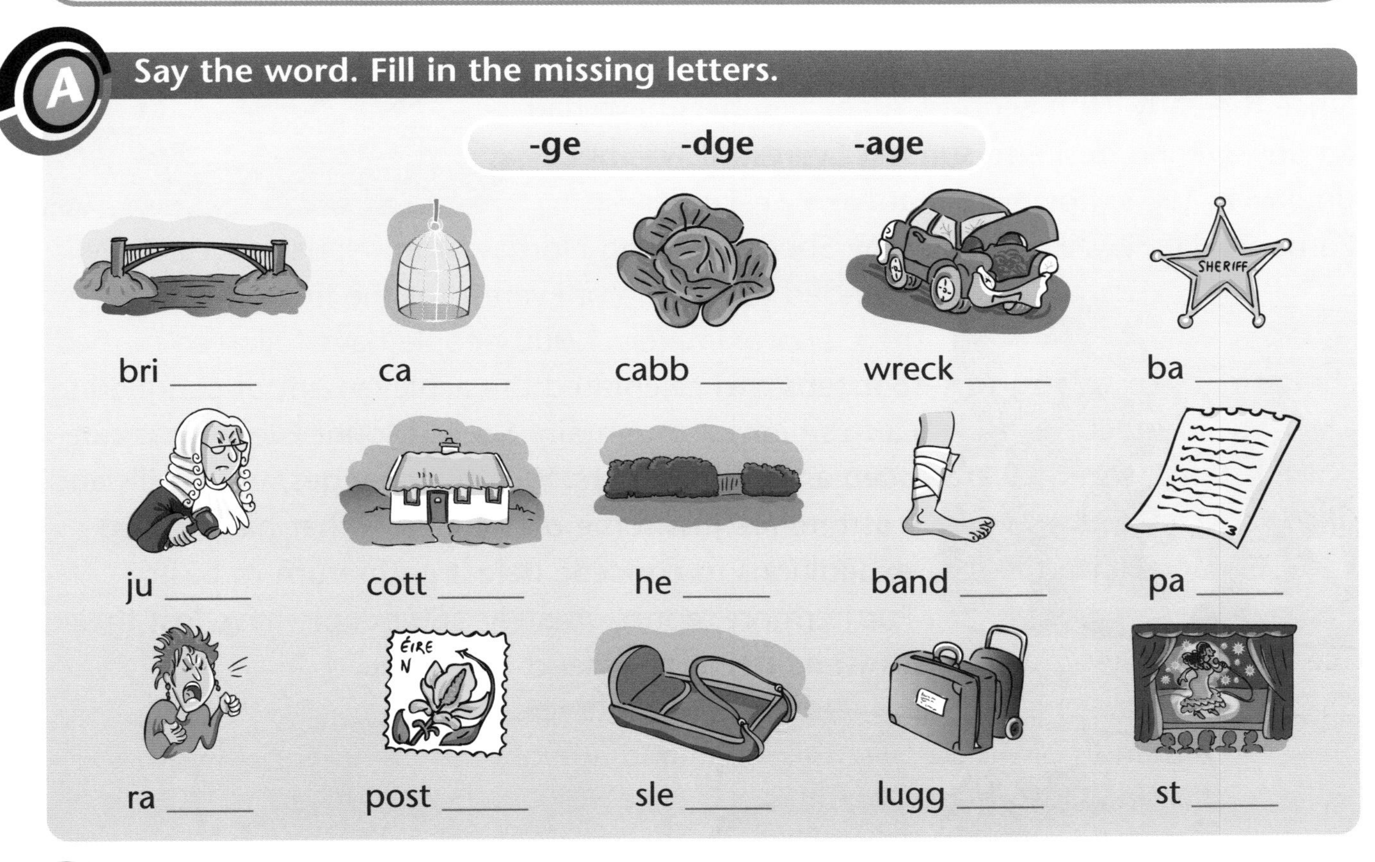

bri ____ ca ____ cabb ____ wreck ____ ba ____

ju ____ cott ____ he ____ band ____ pa ____

ra ____ post ____ sle ____ lugg ____ st ____

B Add the correct ending to complete the word.

Use your dictionary to help you.

lar ____	le ____	do ____
ri ____	aver ____	encour ____
mess ____	wa ____	lo ____
im ____	short ____	man ____
hu ____	fu ____	we ____
pack ____	char ____	mi ____
pass ____	smu ____	outr ____

C Find these words in your dictionary. Write them in sentences.

voyage: ____________________

sludge: ____________________

cadge: ____________________

trudge: ____________________

grudge: ____________________

forge: ____________________

Mount Everest

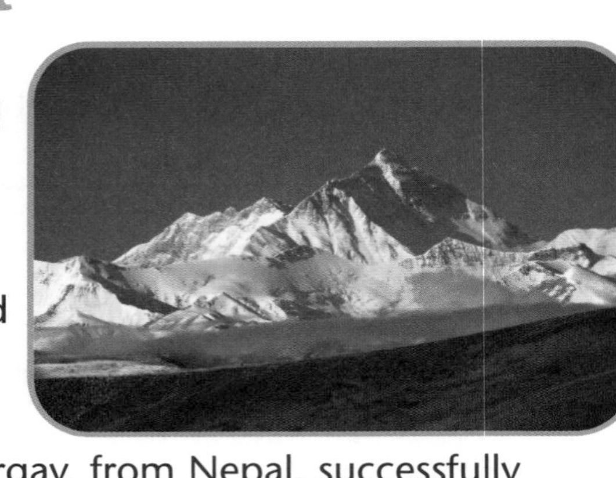

Mount Everest, the world's highest peak, stands at 29,035 feet, or 8,850 metres, on the border of Nepal and Tibet. It is one of several peaks which form the Himalayan mountain range.

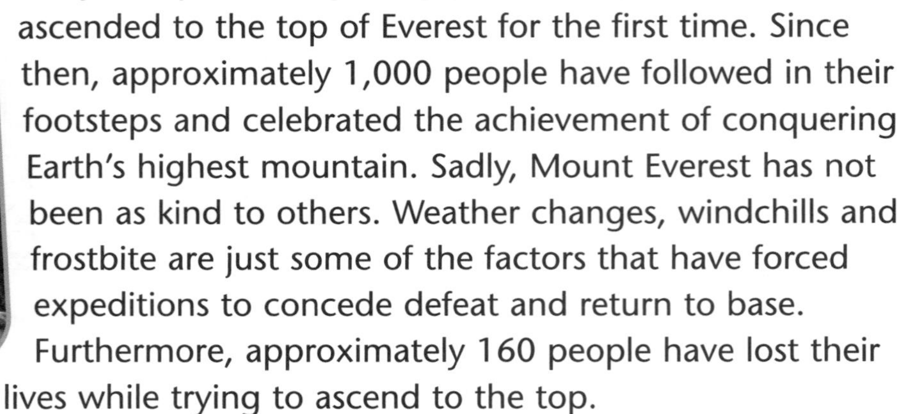

Since the early 19th century, many climbers have had an unwavering desire to summit Everest. It was not until May 1953, however, that New Zealander Sir Edmund Hillary, accompanied by Sherpa Tenzing Norgay, from Nepal, successfully ascended to the top of Everest for the first time. Since then, approximately 1,000 people have followed in their footsteps and celebrated the achievement of conquering Earth's highest mountain. Sadly, Mount Everest has not been as kind to others. Weather changes, windchills and frostbite are just some of the factors that have forced expeditions to concede defeat and return to base. Furthermore, approximately 160 people have lost their lives while trying to ascend to the top.

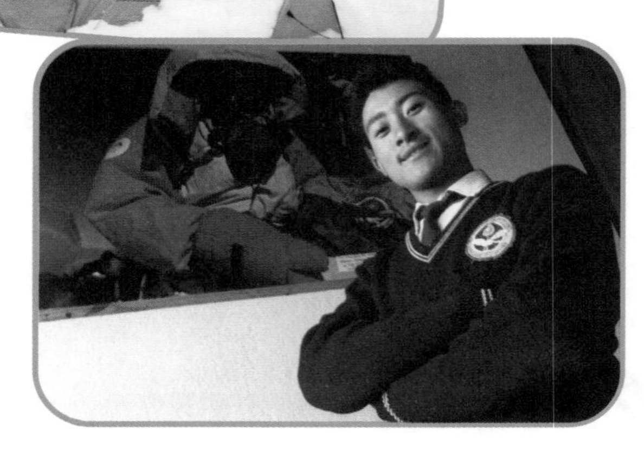

Sherpas are natives of Nepal and Tibet. They are experienced climbers who often act as guides. Their work includes carrying the belongings of the climbers and setting up camps. Temba Tsheri, a Sherpa, knows only too well the gruelling challenges posed to climbers who attempt to reach the summit. In 2000, at the age of fifteen, Temba attempted to be the youngest person in history to climb Everest. He was part of an expedition that included his father and older brother. Unfortunately, deteriorating weather, exhaustion and frostbite deterred him from achieving his goal. In fact, the frostbite on his hands was so severe that doctors had to amputate five of his fingers. A year later, a determined Temba set off once more on his quest to be Everest's youngest climber. He realised his dream in May 2001, aged sixteen years and fourteen days.

1. How high is Mount Everest?
2. Where is Mount Everest located?
3. In what mountain range is Mount Everest?
4. Who were the first people to successfully reach the top of Mount Everest?
5. List some factors that have prevented climbers from reaching the top of Mount Everest.
6. What deterred Temba from reaching the top of Mount Everest on his first attempt to climb it?
7. What physical effect did Temba's first attempt to climb Mount Everest have on him?
8. What age was Temba when he reached the top?

1. You are Sir Edmund Hillary. Describe your thoughts when you reached the summit.
2. Make a list of the equipment that you think would be necessary for climbing Mount Everest.
3. What is a Sherpa? Use the Internet to find out about another Sherpa. Write a paragraph about him or her.
4. What words would you use to describe Temba?
5. Would you like to climb Mount Everest? Give reasons for your answer.

Match the following words to their correct meaning.

unwavering	to remove
summit	highest point or part of a mountain
accompany	to discourage or prevent
ascend	extremely severe or tiring
gruelling	to make or become worse
deteriorate	to be strong, determined
deter	to climb or go up
amputate	to go or be with

Use the Internet to find out the following facts about Mount Everest.

1. Who was the first woman to climb Mount Everest?
2. Who was the first blind person to climb Mount Everest?
3. Who was the fastest person to climb Mount Everest?
4. Who stayed the longest at the top of Mount Everest?
5. What was the biggest expedition to climb Mount Everest?

Explain That!

If we ask a question and need to find an explanation for something we look it up in a dictionary, an encyclopaedia, factual books or on the Internet.

Consider the following question: Why do geese fly in a 'V' shape?

Scientists have determined that the V-shaped formation that geese use when migrating serves two important purposes.

First, it conserves their energy. Each bird flies slightly above the bird in front of it, resulting in a reduction of wind resistance. The birds take turns being in the front, falling back when they get tired. In this way, the geese can travel for a long time before they need to rest, similar to cyclists in a race.

The second benefit of the V-shaped formation is that it is easy to keep track of every bird in the group. Fighter pilots often use this formation for the same reason.

(For more explanations, look up www.loc.gov/rr/scitech/mysteries.)

B Read these scientific questions.

Who invented electricity?

Why does chopping an onion make you cry?

What is the fastest land animal?

Why does pepper make you sneeze?

Why is the ocean blue?

Why do cats purr?

Why do astronauts float in space?

What is the largest flower in the world?

Why do many products in shops have barcodes?

Why does it rain?

Choose one of these scientific questions and write an explanation for it.

Use the following grid to help you plan your piece of writing.

What I know	What I want to know	Where I will do research	What I have learned

Conjunctions are joining words.
They join words, phrases or sentences together,
e.g. I was delighted. I won the race.
I was delighted **when** I won the race.

Fill in the gaps, using the most suitable conjunctions.

when because so until if but before and

1 'No dessert __________ you finish your dinner,' warned Dad.
2 I would like to go to the party __________ I am busy that day.
3 Sam put on his coat __________ going outside to play.
4 The children were late for school __________ the bus broke down.
5 Lucy fell off the swing __________ broke her arm.
6 Everybody was excited __________ we won the football league.
7 I turned on the radio __________ I could listen to music.
8 'You can come to play at my house on Saturday _______ you are allowed.'

B Join the sentences together, using suitable conjunctions.

1 We had to play inside. It was raining.
2 I read a book. I was waiting.
3 I like football. I don't like basketball.
4 Don't climb the wall. You might fall.
5 I would love it. You could come to visit.
6 I do my homework. I come home from school.
7 You won't do well in the test. You study for it.
8 This is my brother Pete. This is my sister Kate.

Find the conjunctions. Rearrange the letters next to each conjunction to find something that you can have fun with. (Answers on page 96.)

a = but	b = house	c = sock	d = apple
e = and	f = cow	g = seven	h = table
i = so	j = running	k = myself	l = although
m = unless	n = since	o = until	p = or
q = stream	r = if	s = lovely	t = because
u = football	v = pen	w = eat	x = funny
y = red	z = quickly		

Answer: t _ _ _ _ _ _ _ _ _

The Marrog

My desk's at the back of the class
And nobody nobody knows
I'm a marrog from Mars
With a body of brass
And seventeen fingers and toes.
Wouldn't they shriek if they knew
I've three eyes at the back of my head
And my hair is bright purple
My nose is deep blue
And my teeth are half yellow half red?
My five arms are silver with knives on them sharper than spears.
I could go back right now if I liked –
And return in a million light years.
I could gobble them all for
I'm seven foot tall
And I'm breathing green flames from my ears.
Wouldn't they yell if they knew
If they guessed that a Marrog was here?
Ha-ha they haven't a clue –
Or wouldn't they tremble with fear!
Look, look, a Marrog
They'd all scream – and SMACK.
The blackboard would fall and the ceiling would crack
And the teacher would faint I suppose.
But I grin to myself sitting right at the back
And Nobody nobody knows.

R.C. Scriven

Let's talk!

- Where is the Marrog from?
- Describe the appearance of the Marrog.
- Neither the children nor the teacher can see the Marrog. In your opinion, why is this?
- Do you think the Marrog would like to be seen?
- What kind of character is the Marrog? Give reasons for your answer.
- Think of other words for these:

  desk shriek gobble tremble grin
- Work in groups of five. Prepare a still image of a scene when the Marrog reveals himself to the teacher and to the class.

- Words are made up of sounds.
- Each sound is called a **syllable**.
- Every **syllable** must have a **vowel**.

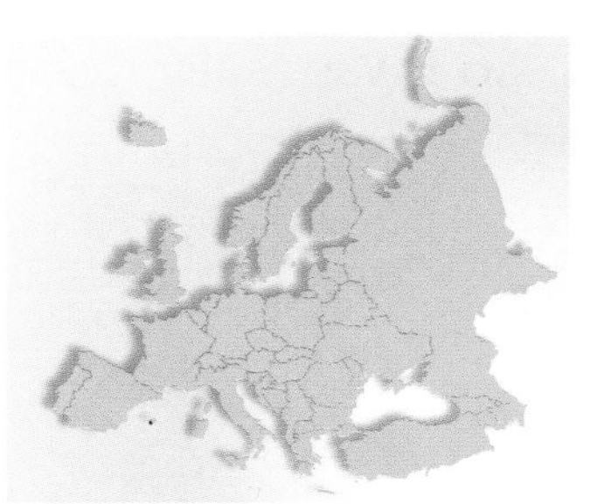

con-tin-ent

te-le-vis-ion

Read the words in the wordbank. How many syllables are in these words? Write the words in the correct column.

party festival song heavy acrobat circus boat swing
rocket suitable chair table suddenly howled edible computer
books mountain grove seasonal story certainly section light

1 syllable	2 syllables	3 syllables

Match the syllables to make words.

de	low	foll	happ	phant
tur	tle	un	tau	rant
chim	lay	res	e	ful
tur	port	fab	u	lous
trans	ful	lux	ow	er
carr	key	el	ti	ry
fel	low	be	ginn	phone
sup	ney	batt	er	y
al	y	tel	e	er
care	per	beau	u	y

Sports Day

Extract from Who's A Big Bully Then? *by Michael Morpurgo*

It was Sports Day. I've never been much good at ball games, like football or basketball or volleyball. I just get pushed around all the time. But running, that's a different thing altogether. I can 'go like a whippet', that's what my father says. So I was really looking forward to Sports Day.

My best distance is 200 metres. I'd got through my heats easily enough and there I was lined up in the sun for the final. There were eight of us all ready and waiting for the gun. And right beside me, in the next lane, was Darren Bishop. This was my chance and I was going to take it.

My father had come to watch. He hardly ever comes into school. He's always too busy on the farm, but he always comes to see me run on Sports Day. And I know why too. He loves to see me win.

He was pretty fast himself when he was a kid. That's what he tells me anyway ...

'Go on, son,' he was shouting. 'You can do it. Don't look around, son. Run low out of the blocks. Get those legs pumping.'

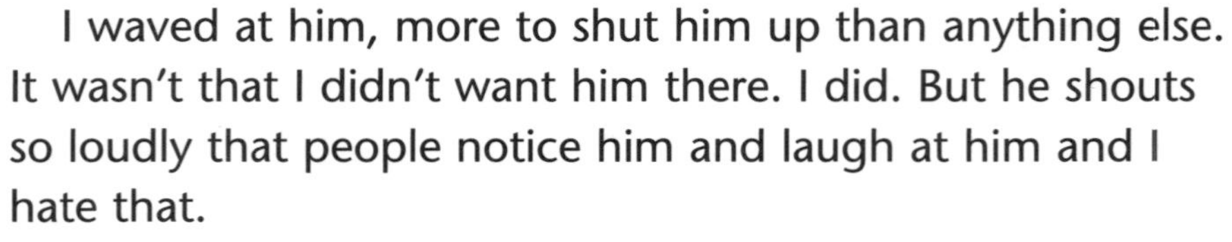

I waved at him, more to shut him up than anything else. It wasn't that I didn't want him there. I did. But he shouts so loudly that people notice him and laugh at him and I hate that.

Darren Bishop had noticed him and was laughing at him. 'What a nerd! Your Dad, he looks a right nerd.' And he said it loud enough for everyone to hear. 'Is he drunk or something?'

I was really riled up, but I made myself look the other way and say nothing. Darren hadn't finished with me yet.

'What's it like to have a little git for a Dad?' he went on. 'Two little gits in the same family. Three maybe. Your Mum's a little git too, isn't she?'

That was it. I'd had enough. I turned on him like an angry terrier. If it was a fight he wanted, then he could have one, right now. It was only the starter who saved me.

'Are you ready? To your marks. Get set.'

Bang! We were off. I was really fired up, but not to win. I didn't care about winning the race any more. All I wanted to do was beat big Darren Bishop. I just wanted to whip him in front of everyone.

He went storming off. He was already miles ahead and going like a train. But I knew he'd gone off too fast. I hung back and just let him think he was winning, let him puff himself right out.

The crowd was going wild, because they could see what Darren couldn't see. I was coming up through the field, going faster and faster all the time, until there was only Darren left to overtake.

Then I was right alongside him, and big Darren Bishop was beginning to slow, beginning to tire. He glanced across at me and I could see in his eyes that he knew he was beaten.

'You don't look so good,' I said. 'You feeling all right? Long way to go yet, long way for a big lump like you.' And I just cruised past him and away from him, waving as I went.

1 What was the boy's favourite sport?
2 What did his father compare him to?
3 Why did his father come to school on Sports Day?
4 Why was he not happy when his father shouted advice at the starting line?
5 How did Darren Bishop insult the boy's family?
6 What was the boy's plan for the race?
7 Do you think the crowd was pleased for him? Explain your answer.
8 What did the boy do as he passed Darren Bishop?

1 Find out what a 'whippet' is.
2 Why, do you think, was the boy eager to beat Darren Bishop?
3 Make a list of words that you would use to describe Darren Bishop.
4 How do you know that Darren Bishop was successful in making the boy angry?
5 Do you think the feeling of anger helped the boy during the race?
6 In your opinion, how did the boy feel when he had won the race?
7 How, do you think, did Darren Bishop feel after the race?
8 Write four sentences describing what you think may have happened next.

True or False?

1 The boy's father said he could 'run like the wind'. ______
2 The boy's best distance was 400 metres. ______
3 The boy's father always came to Sports Day. ______
4 Darren Bishop was friendly towards the boy. ______
5 Darren tried to upset the boy before the race. ______
6 The boy had a clever plan to win the race. ______
7 Darren Bishop paced himself during the race. ______
8 Darren Bishop knew that he was beaten. ______

Character Profiles

Build up the character profiles of Darren Bishop and the boy from the story *Sports Day*, using the words in the box. You may add other words.

Darren Bishop
e.g. boastful

angry	weak
haughty	focused
nervous	strong
insecure	proud
jealous	boastful

Boy
e.g. focused

Look at these pictures carefully. Give names to the characters.

Build a profile for each character by making a list of words or phrases which you think best suits them.

Choose one of the characters from B. Write a short story in which your character takes the main role. Use your list of words to help you.

Create a setting for the story. You may include other characters.

Here are some points to consider:

- your character's name
- setting – where is the story taking place?
- scenario – what is happening/going to happen?
- does your character meet other characters?
- outcome – how does your short story end?

Singular means **one** thing. **Plural** means **more than one** thing.

- To make most words **plural**, add an 's',
  e.g. *one dog* → *many dogs*
- For most words ending in 'sh', 'ch', 's', 'z' or 'x' add an 'es',
  e.g. *one branch* → *several branches*
  one fox → *two foxes*

A Rewrite these sentences in the plural.

1. The witch cast a spell on the young girl and boy.
2. The teacher put the book on the table.
3. Jenny looked at the dress and jacket in the shop window.
4. The girl found the watch hidden behind the bush.
5. Carol put the broken cup and glass into the box.
6. The class had fun at the football match.
7. The girl went to the quiz.
8. The hungry boy ate the apple and the peach.

- For words ending in a consonant and 'y', drop the 'y' and add 'ies',
  e.g. *one family* → *two families.*
- For most words ending in 'f' or 'fe', drop the 'f' or 'fe' and add 'ves',
  e.g. *one knife* → *some knives.*
- **Rule breakers:** Some words are different. To make them plural you just add an 's',
  e.g. *dwarf* *roof* *chief* *cliff.*

B Change these words from singular to plural.

pony	half	party	shelf
fly	elf	wolf	jelly
wife	spy	roof	cherry
army	life	copy	dwarf
chief	lady	scarf	story

C Write the plural of the nouns in these pictures.

Valentia Lighthouse

Valerie O'Sullivan

Let's talk!

- What building can you see in the photograph?
- Why, do you think, was this building built here?
- In what way does this building help boats and ships?
- List the names and locations of some other lighthouses around the coast of Ireland.
- With a partner, make a list of as many adjectives as you can that describe the sea in the photograph. You may use your dictionary/thesaurus to help you.
- Now, make a list of verbs associated with the sea, e.g. the sea roared; the sea crashed.
- Choose adjectives and verbs to construct sentences about the sea.
- Create a story based on the photograph. Start with: 'Only the crashing waves broke the eerie silence as we waited anxiously for Dad's trawler to return...

Brain Teaser Make a list words that rhyme with 'crime'.

- A **prefix** is a letter or group of letters placed before the root word.

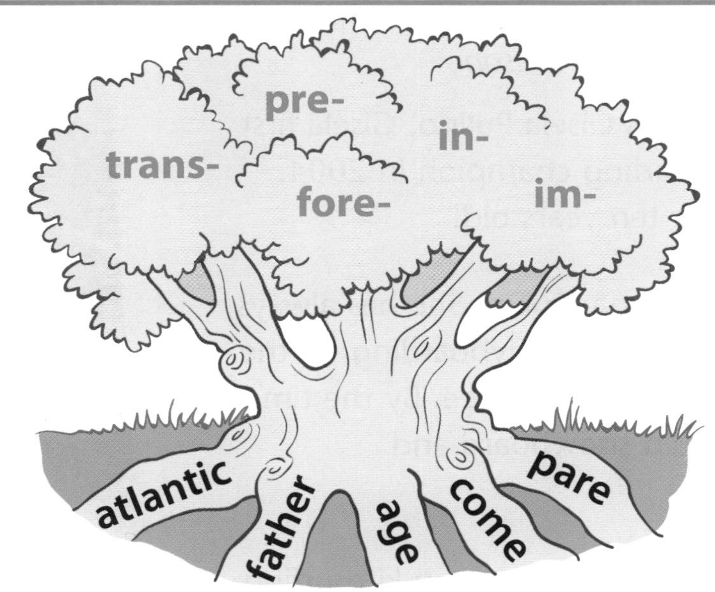

A Write the root words.

increase ______	inactive ______	incapable ______	insane ______
imprison ______	imprint ______	impossible ______	impulse ______
forehead ______	foreman ______	foremost ______	forecast ______
prevent ______	prefix ______	present ______	prepay ______
transform ______	transport ______	transact ______	translate ______

B Write the word, using the correct prefix for these root words:

in- **im-** **fore-** **pre-** **trans-**

______-side	______-direct	______-proper	______-scribe
______-finger	______-mediate	______-press	______-patient
______-port	______-habit	______-land	______-formal
______-serve	______-view	______-former	______-dependent
______-prove	______-tend	______-sect	______-mature
______-mit	______-fer	______-parent	______-sight

C Write some more words, using these prefixes. Use your dictionary to help you.

in ______	im ______	fore ______	pre ______	trans ______
in ______	im ______	fore ______	pre ______	trans ______
in ______	im ______	fore ______	pre ______	trans ______
in ______	im ______	fore ______	pre ______	trans ______

Gisela Pulido – Kitesurfer

Extract from 21st Century Lives: Extreme Sports People
by Paul Mason

Kitesurfing's biggest star is Gisela Pulido. Gisela first became the world kitesurfing champion in 2004. Amazingly, she was just ten years old!

Gisela was born in Barcelona, Spain. She has always been sports-mad, and started bodyboarding on the city's beaches when she was just three. By the time she was five, Gisela could snowboard and skateboard as well.

Around this time, Gisela's father took up kitesurfing. She dreamed of trying the sport, and making the huge jumps and spins in the air she saw the kitesurfers performing. But Gisela was too small! She needed to weigh at least 35kg to be allowed to use kitesurfing equipment.

Finally, in 2000, Gisela passed the 35kg barrier and was able to try kitesurfing. She quickly became an expert. To help Gisela's kitesurfing get even better, her family moved from Barcelona to Tarifa, on Spain's southern coast. Tarifa is famous for its windy conditions. Windsurfers and kitesurfers come from all round the world to sail there.

Gisela also started at a different school, which finished at 2pm. This was a big change from the school that she had attended previously which had finished at 5pm. The change meant that Gisela was able to train much harder than before. All the training began to pay off. In 2004, when Gisela was ten, she won the Kitesurfing World Championships for the first time. This was despite most of the other competitors being between two and three times her age! She carried on her great success. In 2005, Gisela won five of the six contests for the world's top kitesurfers. To cap it all, she again won the World Championship at the end of the year.

Gisela's dreams for the future include the hope that kitesurfing might be an Olympic sport one day. If this happens, she will be hoping to win an Olympic kitesurfing gold, to go with her World Championship trophies!

Comprehension

1. What age was Gisela when she became the world kitesurfing champion in 2004?
2. Where was Gisela born?
3. What did Gisela achieve by the time she was (a) three years old and (b) five years old?
4. What weight does a person need to be to use kitesurfing equipment?
5. How did Gisela's family help her to get better at kitesurfing?
6. How did being at school in Tarifa help with Gisela's training?
7. What successes did Gisela have in 2005?
8. What are Gisela's dreams for the future?

1. Why, do you think, did Gisela become so interested in skateboarding, bodyboarding and kitesurfing?
2. What adjectives would you use to describe Gisela?
3. For Gisela, what was the advantage of living by the beach?
4. Make a list of other watersports.
5. Use your atlas to find (a) Barcelona and (b) Tarifa.
6. Name five Olympic sports.
7. Gisela's dream for the future is to be an Olympic kitesurfer. Write about your dreams for the future.
8. Use books or the Internet to find out more about kitesurfing. Use the information that you have gathered to produce a leaflet promoting kitesurfing.

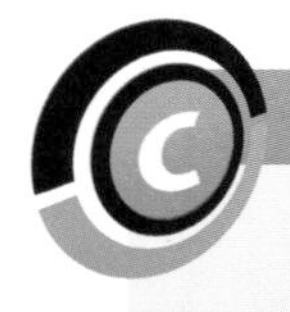

Do you know any other sports stars who achieved great success at a young age? Choose one person and find out about him/her. Write his/her profile.

Extension Work

1. Conduct a survey on the different sports played by the children in your class. Present your findings on a graph.
2. Write a paragraph about your favourite sport. Read it to the class.
3. Find out what sports are available in your local area.
4. Choose one local sporting hero. Write about him/her.

Being a Reporter

A report is a piece of writing that gives us information about people, events, animals, places and objects. We can read reports in newspapers, magazines, journals, factual books, encyclopaedias, and on the Internet.

Name three examples of each of the following:

1 newspaper
2 magazine
3 factual book

Reports are written by newspaper reporters or journalists. Before writing a report on a particular topic, reporters must first gather information. They do this by interviewing one or more persons, researching books and/or the Internet. Sometimes, they visit a place to do their research.

Pretend that you are a reporter. Think of a famous person that you would like to interview. Plan and write a report about that person.

Use the following framework to help you:

Name: ____________________

Occupation: ____________________

Lives in: ____________________

____

Family: ____________________

____

Reasons for being famous: ____________________

____

____

Qualities: ____________________

____

____

- To make most words ending in **'o' plural**, add an **'es'**,
  e.g. *one hero → two heroes.*
- **Rule breakers:** For words ending in two vowels, only add an **'s'**,
  e.g. *one video → several videos.*
- For most foreign words ending in **'o'**, add only an **'s'**,
  e.g. *one piano → many pianos.*

A Write the passage and make the highlighted words plural.

Jake and Jenny climbed the *volcano*. They were exhausted. They decided to rest and eat the *tomato, avocado* and *potato* in their lunch bag. Jake played a game with his *domino*. Jenny listened to the *soprano* singing on her *stereo.* She also listened to *cello* and *piano*.

Suddenly they heard a strange sound. They were terrified. When they realised it was the *echo* from the nearby *cuckoo* and *buffalo*, they felt very silly.

- Some words change completely in the **plural**,
  e.g. *one child → two children.*
- Other words do not change in the **plural**,
  e.g. *one fish → five fish.*

B Write the plural of these nouns.

man	____________	mouse	____________
sheep	____________	woman	____________
cod	____________	deer	____________
tooth	____________	foot	____________
trout	____________	goose	____________

C Rewrite the following sentences correctly.

1. The three man counted six sheeps and four deers in the field.
2. I broke a teeth when I tripped over my left feet.
3. The young childs ate their potatos and trouts.
4. The buffalo were terrified of the tornados.
5. The women put her new goldfishes into their bowl.
6. The heros in the film were very brave.
7. My sister always buys different shampooes for her hair.
8. My teacher took some photoes of our class playing the banjoes.

Proverbs

Proverbs are short, memorable sayings that often contain facts or words of wisdom.

1 Many countries have their own proverbs.
  (a) Find an Irish proverb.
  (b) Find a Chinese proverb.

2 Read the following proverbs. Discuss their meanings. (Answers on page 97.)
  (a) A bad workman blames his tools.
  (b) As the old cock crows, the young cock learns.
  (c) The schoolhouse bell sounds bitter in youth and sweet in old age.
  (d) You'll never plough a field by turning it over in your mind.
  (e) The wheel is always turning.
  (f) Necessity is the mother of invention.
  (g) You can't put an old head on young shoulders.
  (h) The early bird catches the worm.

Read each proverb and match it to the picture that you think best describes its meaning. **(Answers on page 97.)**

(a) A stitch in time saves nine.

(b) A watched pot never boils.

(c) Praise the young and it will come.

(d) Once bitten, twice shy.

(e) Two shorten the road.

Use books and/or the Internet to find out more proverbs.

Interview older people and ask them if they know any old sayings or proverbs.

Brain Teaser Answer: Sweet. Give **five** possible questions.

- A suffix is a letter or group of letters added to the end of a root word.

-ing -able -er -ed -en -est

- If the root word ends in two consonants, just add on the suffix.

jumping singer

- If the root word has a short vowel and one consonant, double the consonant and add the suffix.

winning swimmer

- If the root word ends in e, drop the e before adding the suffix beginning with a vowel,

e.g. rid**e** + ing = riding write**e** + er = writer

A Add suffixes to these words to make new words.

1 dive ______
2 love ______
3 save ______
4 value ______
5 brave ______
6 make ______
7 excite ______
8 like ______
9 fine ______
10 compare ______

- If the suffix begins with a consonant, just add the suffix to the root word,

e.g. love + ly = lovely hope + ful = hopeful

-ful -s -ly -ment -less -ness -ship

B Add suffixes to these words to make new words.

friend ______	sad ______	forget ______
help ______	judge ______	use ______
hope ______	faith ______	slow ______
shape ______	truth ______	content ______
kind ______	late ______	excite ______
lone ______	pave ______	relation ______

The Widow O'Brien

Extract from Fields of Home *by Marita Conlon-McKenna*

'Good times and bad times I've had under this roof,' Agnes whispered, 'but I never imagined it ending like this.' Tears ran down her cheeks as Nano escorted her out into the sunlight. Eily ran from the crowd and helped Mary-Brigid lift out the parcelled-up blanket and the sheet-wrapped crockery. The crowd hushed, as the Widow O'Brien left her cottage for the last time. Then, one by one, the neighbours began to file past her, each offering her their condolences and wishing her well in the future.

The bailiff strode by them all into the low cottage, and was amazed to find so few possessions.

'You'll hold on there, sir!' warned the older constable. 'We wouldn't want you to damage any of the lady's valuables.'

'Valuables!' jeered the bailiff. 'There's nothing of value here.'

Dermot O'Reilly, who lived about two miles down the road, had arrived with a donkey and cart. 'Mrs O'Brien, if you give the say-so, I'll put whatever you want on the cart and I'll be pleased to drop you wherever you wish.'

Mary-Brigid watched as they loaded up the few bits and pieces.

'Will ye not come home for a sup of tea and a piece of bread with us, Agnes?' pleaded Nano. 'You wouldn't mind, Eily, sure you wouldn't?'

''Tis all right, Nano. You've done more than enough,' murmured the poor widow woman before Eily had a chance to speak. 'I'm best to get into the town to try and find somewhere to stay.' She raised her voice. 'They can tumble my cottage, tear it down stone by stone, but they can't take away the fact that me and mine lived and died there. I have two sons and, would you believe it, eight grandchildren. The O'Briens will always be a part of this place. No-one can change that!'

Nano stood proudly as her old friend turned to her neighbours and friends and said goodbye. The crowd all watched her climb onto her cart and set off over the rough ground to the roadway, her face almost see-through, the thin shawl wrapped around her head and shoulders.

'What will happen to her now, Mammy? Where will she go?' sobbed Mary-Brigid, hot tears stinging her face and throat.

'I'm not sure, pet. The sons might send her some money and maybe she'll rent a room someplace, or she'll get a place in the Union home for the destitute!' murmured Eily sadly. 'To tell the truth, Mary-Brigid, I don't rightly know!'

'It's not fair! They shouldn't have done it!' shouted Mary-Brigid, anger burning in her young heart. She knew that she would never forget this terrible day.

1. What belongings did Agnes have with her when leaving her cottage?
2. Why did the crowd hush?
3. How did the neighbours show their support for Agnes?
4. Did Agnes have many possessions?
5. How did Dermot O'Reilly offer to help Agnes?
6. Where did Agnes decide to go?
7. How many grandchildren did Agnes have?
8. What effect did the incident have on Mary-Brigid?

1. Why, do you think, was Agnes made to leave her home?
2. In your opinion, how did Agnes feel about leaving her home?
3. Use your dictionary to find out what is (a) a constable and (b) a bailiff.
4. Write five adjectives to describe (a) the constable and (b) the bailiff from the story.
5. Where might Agnes' family have been?
6. In your opinion, what kind of character is Agnes?
7. Discuss how the different characters felt in the story. Prepare a still image of the eviction scene.
8. What, do you think, may have happened to Agnes afterwards?

Extension Work

Use the Internet and/or books to find out about the Great Famine in Ireland.

Find out the meaning of the following words:

- blight
- Black '47
- coffin ships
- workhouse
- eviction
- soup-kitchen

Eye-witness Accounts

Read this eye-witness account written by James Mahoney, a Cork artist.

In 1847, James Mahoney was asked by a London newspaper to write an article about the state of Co. Cork during the Great Famine.

'I started from Cork, by the mail, for Skibbereen and saw little until we came to Clonakilty, where the coach stopped for breakfast; and here, for the first time, the horrors of the poverty became visible, in the vast number of famished poor who flocked around the coach to beg alms: amongst them was a woman carrying in her arms the corpse of a fine child, and making the most distressing appeal to the passengers for aid to enable her to purchase a coffin and bury her dear little baby. This horrible spectacle induced me to make some inquiry about her, when I learned from the people of the hotel that each day brings dozens of such applicants into the town. After leaving Clonakilty, each step that we took westward brought fresh evidence of the truth of the reports of the misery, as we either met a funeral or a coffin at every hundred yards, until we approached the country of the Shepperton Lakes. Here, the distress became more striking, from the decrease of numbers at the funerals, none having more than eight or ten attendants, and many only two or three.'

Discuss the following questions and write the answers.

1 Do you think James Mahoney gives a good description of what he saw?
2 What was the most distressing thing he saw in Clonakilty?
3 What did he find more distressing at Shepperton Lakes?
4 Is this a good eye-witness account of Ireland during the famine? Give reasons for your answer.

Write an eye-witness account.

Pretend that you are Mary-Brigid from the novel *Fields of Home*. Use the grid to help you plan an eye-witness account of the Widow O'Brien's eviction. Write the account.

Setting: ______________________

Time: ______________________

People: ______________________

What happened? ______________________

Outcome: ______________________

A **sentence** is a group of words which must:

- make sense together
- begin with a capital letter
- end with a full stop, question mark or exclamation mark.

Unjumble these sentences:

1 visit friend my went I to in sick hospital the
2 bought in shoes shop new Lucy the
3 capital Tokyo the is Japan of
4 like with play I to friends my basketball
5 brought in dog a walk his park the Pete for

Finish these sentences:

1 I want to go ____.
2 My teacher is ____.
3 The guard chased ____.
4 The car was ____.
5 Kate likes to ____.

- A **paragraph** is a group of sentences about one main idea.
- When you are writing a story you should sort your ideas into paragraphs.

Rewrite the story, using three paragraphs.

Sharks are cold-blooded creatures that can be found in many seas and oceans all over the world. They are clever animals and have very good memories. Sharks move quickly and easily through water by sweeping their tails from side to side. They can hear, see and smell very well. There are many different types of sharks. The largest shark in the world is the whale shark. They can measure up to eighteen metres and their mouths can be over a metre wide. The basking shark is the largest shark in Irish waters and can reach over nine metres in length. Many people think that sharks are extremely dangerous and frequently attack humans. However, most sharks avoid people and would not harm them. The most dangerous sharks are the Great Whites – they have attacked people swimming or surfing. If you think a shark is getting too close, a punch in the nose will often frighten it away!

I, Too

I, too, sing America.

I am the darker brother.
They send me to eat in the kitchen
When company comes,
But I laugh,
And eat well,
And grow strong.

Tomorrow
I'll sit at the table
When company comes.
Nobody'll dare
Say to me,
'Eat in the kitchen,'
Then.

Besides,
They'll see how beautiful I am
And be ashamed –

I, too, am America.

Langston Hughes

Let's talk!

- Is this is a modern poem? Give reasons for your answer.
- Who, do you think, is speaking in the poem?
- What words would you use to describe the speaker in the poem?
- What does the speaker mean by 'I, too, sing America' in the first verse?
- In your opinion, who are 'they' in the first verse?
- Who might the 'company' be?
- In your opinion, why is the speaker sent to the kitchen to eat?
- Who, do you think, sent the speaker to the kitchen?
- How does the speaker's mood change in Verses 2 and 3?
- In the final verse what does the speaker mean by 'I, too, am America'?
- Role-play! Work in groups of six. Dramatise the scene when the 'company' arrives and the speaker is sent to the kitchen to eat.
- Dramatise the scene when the speaker stands up for himself.

Say the word. Fill in the missing letters.

er ir ur ear

p _____ l	n _____ se	sk _____ t	s _____ vant	sw _____ ve

b _____ row	_____ th	s _____ fer	st _____	m _____ maid

l _____ ner	p _____ se	b _____ ry	sh _____ t	h _____ se

Fill in the missing letters to complete the word.

Use your dictionary to help you.

st _____ n	d _____ t	c _____ ve
_____ ly	m _____ cy	_____ thquake
c _____ cle	s _____ vive	f _____ niture
b _____ th	s _____ geon	b _____ st
f _____ st	res _____ ch	s _____ face
c _____ cus	c _____ tain	th _____ d
t _____ rier	reh _____ se	dist _____ b

Find these words in your dictionary. Write them in sentences.

birch: ____

dreary: ____

yearn: ____

heron: ____

survey: ____

surpass: ____

Brochures

Multi Sports Camp

www.letsgo.ie

Dear Parents

Welcome to Let's Go!

We are your No.1 choice for summer camps in Ireland. Our programmes have been tried and tested over the last 25 years and we can offer your child a week of action, fun and adventure in a safe environment. Your child can participate in new thrilling and exciting activities as well as some of the old firm favourites. To ensure our programmes are taught to the highest of standards our staff are carefully selected from the teaching profession. We look forward to meeting new campers and welcoming back familiar faces to our 2009 Lets Go! summer camps.

Eileen Sheehy BA Phys.Ed and **Kevin O'Brien** BA Phys.Ed
Camp Directors.

Let's Go!
ONLINE
www.letsgo.ie

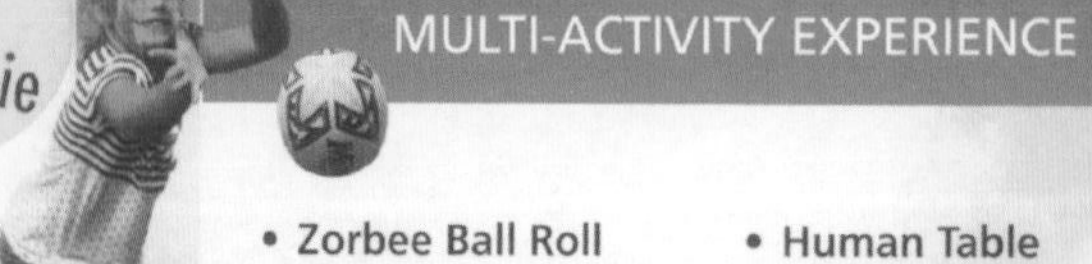

CAMP STRUCTURE

- **Times:** 9.30am – 3.30pm daily
- **Activities:** We offer two programmes: Multi Activity Experience (7-13 years) and Funtime Experience (5-6 years)
- **Groups:** Children will be placed in groups with other children of similar age
- **Lunchbreaks:** Fully supervised

7-13 Years
MULTI-ACTIVITY EXPERIENCE

- **Zorbee Ball Roll**
- **Bungee Trampoline**
- **Wrecking Ball**
- **KMX Karts**
- **Eliminator**
- **Human Table Football**
- **Soccer Shoot**
- **Wobbly Ladder**

- Jenga
- Tug-O-War
- Unicurl
- Crazy Golf
- Hurling/Camogie
- Whuck
- Badminton
- Lacrosse
- Rounders
- Pelmanism
- Fun Orienteering
- Hoppers
- Superstars
- Bouncy Castle
- Parachute Games
- Bocce Bowls
- Soccer
  - Chinese Soccer
  - Crab Soccer
- Football
- Mini Rugby
- Unihoc
- Olympic Handball
- Flingsock Games
- Basketball
- Team Challenge
- Camp Games
- Let's Go! Bingo
- Speed Stacking

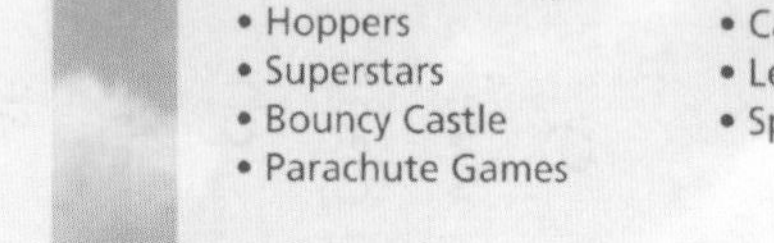

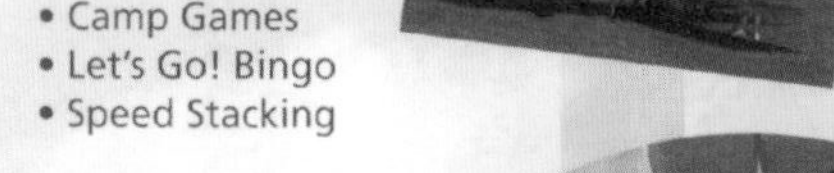

5-6 Years
FUNTIME EXPERIENCE

Fun is the name of the game for our 5 & 6 year old campers. The day's timetable provides the perfect mix of active and passive pursuits. We use smaller playing areas, simplified rules and adapted equipment, to create an environment that is stimulating without being daunting.

- **Bungee Trampoline**
- **Wrecking Ball**
- **Soccer Shoot**
- **Wobbly Ladder**
- **Eliminator**
- **Bouncy Castle**

- Parachute Games
- Scavenger Hunt
- Jenga
- Short Tennis
- Musical Games
- Mini Basketball
- Bean Bag Toss
- Teddy Bear Picnic
- Unihoc
- Songs & Stories
- Crazy Golf
- Camp Games
- Face Painting
- Fun Relays
- Ball Games
- Construction Toys
- Hoppers
- Indoor Bowls
- Tug-O-War
- Skittles
- Buzzy Bingo
- Flingsock Games
- Speed Stacking

LET'S GO MULTI SPORTS

1. What is the name of the camp?
2. At what time does the camp begin?
3. What is the name of the programme for (a) 5–6 year olds, and (b) 7–13 year olds?
4. List five activities that the 7–13 year olds can do.
5. List five activities that the 5–6 year olds can do.
6. Are there any activities that both groups can do?
7. In the 7–13 year old Multi-Activity Experience, name three activites that you would like to try. Why would you like to try each of these?
8. At what time does the camp finish?

1. What is your favourite activity in the 7–13 years Multi-Activity Experience? Give reasons for your answer.
2. What is your least favourite activity in this programme? Why?
3. Can you think of any activities that are not listed on the Multi-Activity Experience programme that you would like to add?
4. Can you think of any activities that are not listed on the Funtime Experience that you would like to add?
5. In your opinion, why are there different programmes for the 5–6 year olds and the 7–13 year olds?
6. Apart from the activities, what else is different about the 5–6 year old Funtime Experience?

What activity is it?

Read each of the following lists of equipment. Write down which activity each list best describes and what programme the activity is featured in.

1. A very long rope, two teams of children pulling at each end of the rope.
2. Paints and lots of faces!
3. A bat, a ball, two teams of children, a large space to play in.
4. Two rackets, one shuttle, two players, a court.
5. Two teams, a plastic hockey stick for each player, one plastic hockey ball, a large space to play in.

Choose any one activity from either programme. Write a paragraph explaining what the activity is.

Writing Brochures

Brochures are used to advertise a service or a product. They usually contain bright colours and clear writing to catch the reader's attention. A logo or symbol that is easily recognised is often used.

Logos

1. Cut out sample logos from newspapers and magazines. Discuss what you like/do not like about them. Make a class collage with these logos.
2. A new pet farm will be opening shortly in your area. Choose a name and design a logo for it.

Design a brochure to advertise the new pet farm, using the name and logo you chose in A.

Fold an A4 sheet of white paper/card in two.

Page 1 – The name and logo should appear on the front.
Page 2 – List the animals and facilities at the new pet farm, e.g. a playground, a petting corner. Include pictures.
Page 3 – List special activities available at the pet farm, e.g. treasure hunts, a bouncing castle.
Page 4 – The back page should contain the opening hours, prices, address and telephone number.

Choose suitable colours for the background and for the writing.

- We send postcards to friends and family when we are on holiday. They are a fun way of letting everybody know how we are getting on.
- Postcards are usually written in a friendly way, so we can use some informal language.

A stamp goes in the top right-hand corner.

Write the name of the person here.

Hi Peter,
I am here with my family in Dungarvan for a week and we are having a great time. There is so much to do! The weather is great so we go swimming every day at the beach. I tried surfing yesterday. It was brilliant!
I am going horse riding today with my brother. Everybody says hello and we will come visit you when we get home.
Bye for now,
Jason

ÉIRE
N

Mr Peter Kelly
25 Whitewall Road
Clonmel
Co. Tipperary
Ireland

Write your news on the left-hand side.

The address goes on the right-hand side.

Sign your name.

Draw postcards in your copy. Write to different friends, telling them about all the things you are doing in these places. Use your imagination!

1 You are having a great time near a beach on a sun holiday in Spain.
2 You are in a ski resort in Italy.
3 You are camping in France but the weather is terrible!
4 You are shopping and sightseeing in New York.

Word Hunt

In your dictionary, find four examples of words containing the following, and write their meanings:

1 words beginning with 'rh'
2 words beginning with 'sch'
3 words beginning with 'au'
4 words ending with 're'
5 words ending with 'gh'
6 words ending with 'ic'

Context Clues

Read the following sentences. Choose the word most similar in meaning to the underlined word.

1 Her passport will <u>expire</u> next year.
(a) be accepted
(b) be denied
(c) be out of date
(d) be changed

2 The athletes found the obstacle course to be <u>rigorous</u>.
(a) easy
(b) exciting
(c) too long
(d) tough

3 The builders checked the <u>stability</u> of the scaffolding.
(a) height
(b) steadiness
(c) weight
(d) materials

4 After the match, the supporters were <u>subdued</u>.
(a) celebrating
(b) delighted
(c) angry
(d) sad

5 The chief executive sent a <u>memorandum</u> to her staff.
(a) message
(b) bunch of flowers
(c) light lunch
(d) book

6 The librarian sorted the books into different <u>categories</u>.
(a) boxes
(b) shelves
(c) groups
(d) rooms

- What is the tenth word in your dictionary?
- What is the twentieth word in your dictionary?
- What is the thirtieth word in your dictionary?
- Put each word into a sentence of its own.

A Fill in the word wheels with words that end in a 'j' sound.

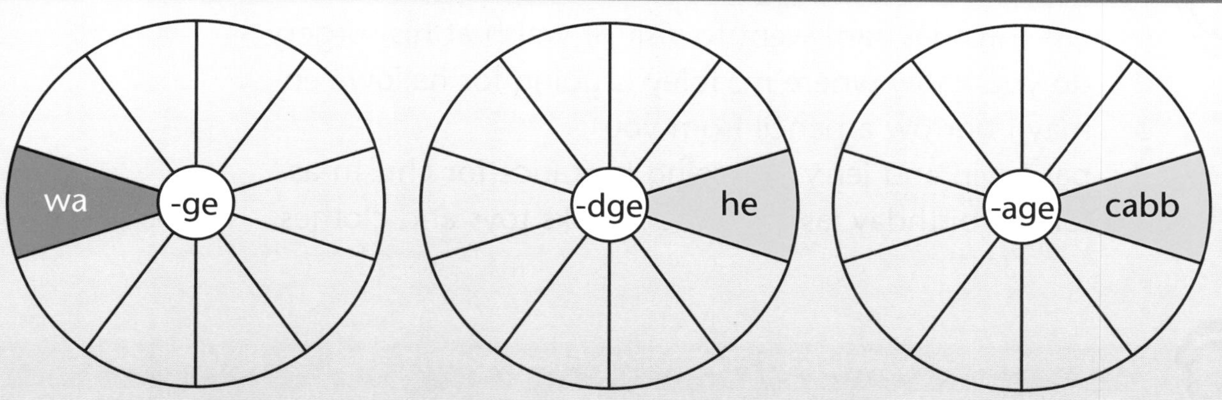

B How many syllables?

elephant	______	inexpensive	______	welcome	______
rainbow	______	brave	______	home	______
surprise	______	ridiculous	______	experiment	______
elbow	______	lovely	______	careful	______
television	______	smile	______	happiness	______

C Prefixes and Suffixes

All of these words have prefixes/suffixes added. Circle the root words.

e.g. impress sadly lightly preside

climbing	forgetful	foreman	impossible	inward	slowly
transfix	insane	friendship	chairs	foretell	judgement
inactive	imperfect	badly	singer	forewarn	older
premature	helpless	hopeful	insincere	pretend	foregone

D Circle the correct spelling: -er, -ir, -ur, -ear.

cercus	certain	lerner	frniture	cercle
circus	cirtain	lirner	firniture	circle
curcus	curtain	lorner	furniture	curcle
cearcus	ceartain	learner	fearniture	cearcle

Rewrite these sentences, using the correct punctuation.

1. last thursday sam went to visit dr walsh at his surgery
2. do you know where mr foley is going for hallowe'en
3. may i borrow a pencil from you
4. pat kevin and jerry are going to france for christmas
5. for my birthday last july i got books toys and clothes

Rewrite these sentences. Underline the nouns and circle the verbs.

1. The baby cried when his toy broke.
2. Paul put his books and copies into his schoolbag.
3. The frog uses his long, sticky tongue to catch food.
4. Melissa and John went to Dublin on a train.
5. I ate my sandwich and drank my juice.

C Choose suitable adjectives for these sentences.

1. The __________ giraffe ate the __________ leaves.
2. I sat in the __________ chair and read a __________ book.
3. The __________ woman is wearing a __________ dress.
4. The __________ teacher scolded the __________ boy.
5. The __________ tractor drove down the __________ lane.

D Change these adjectives to adverbs.

slow	__________	loud	__________
sad	__________	brave	__________
proud	__________	sleepy	__________
hungry	__________	lazy	__________
busy	__________	angry	__________

Fill in the gaps, using a suitable conjunction.

1. The girl did her homework __________ going out to play.
2. We played inside __________ it was raining.
3. The girl read a book __________ she waited for her friend.
4. I will go swimming __________ my dad allows me.
5. I eat broccoli __________ I don't like it.

The European Union

elect	most	currency	environment	Sea	Arctic	billion	Ocean
1973	citizen	population	Brussels	smallest	French	Mediterranean	

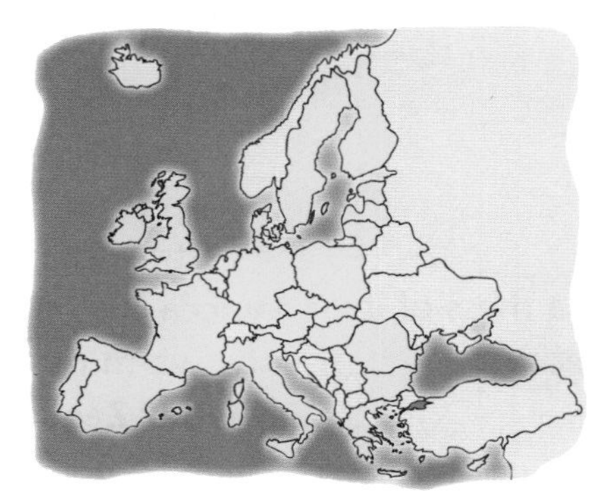

Almost half a ___________ people live in the European Union (EU), making it the world's largest ___________ after China and India. Twenty-five countries are members of the European Union. France has the biggest land area, Germany has the ___________ people and Malta is the ___________.

The European Union's borders stretch from the freezing cold of the ___________ north to the intense heat of the ___________ south, from the Atlantic ___________ to the Aegean ___________.

Ireland joined the European Union in ___________. Every five years, the people of Europe vote to ___________ members to the European Parliament. The last European election was held in June 2009. The Members of Parliament (MEPs) vote on issues like the economy, health, immigration and the ___________. They meet in the ___________ town of Strasbourg for one week every month. The rest of the time, they attend other meetings in ___________, Belgium.

Ireland has 13 MEPs in the European Parliament.

Twelve countries out of the twenty-five EU countries use the euro as their ___________. The eurozone is the name given to the countries that use the euro. Some EU countries are not using the euro but may do so in the future.

If you live in an EU country and you are an EU ___________, you can travel between any of the other EU countries and live in any EU country you wish.

Page 21

Activity C

Tuesday	Missus	Avenue	Father	December
Street	Mister	Sister	Terrace	Wednesday
County	Junior	Senior	Number	kilometre
Grove	Estate	Road	centimetre	October

Funny Sounding Words – page 22

Activity B. Idioms

She made a bags of it! = She made a mess of it.
Let's hit the road! = Let's leave *or* Let's go.
That's a cod! = That's a joke.
Will we make shapes? = Will we go?
He is a sleveen! = He is very sly.
They were throwing shapes = They were messing *or* They were fooling around.

Activity C. Unusual Words

abominable = very unpleasant, bad
bedraggled = untidy
camouflage = to blend in with the background or surroundings
Davy Jones' Locker = the bottom of the sea, according to pirates
entrepreneur = a person who makes money by starting new businesses
flabbergasted = to be very surprised
gobbledygook = complicated language that is difficult to understand
hobbledehoy = a troublesome young person
idiosyncrasy = a person's particular way of behaving or thinking/a distinctive or peculiar feature of a thing
jamboree = a lavish or noisy celebration or party
kibosh = firmly put an end to
laughing stock = a person who is ridiculed by everyone
mackintosh = a full-length, waterproof coat
Nantucket = an island off the coast of Massachusetts, south of Cape Cod, USA
onyx = a precious stone with layers of different colours
paparazzi = photographers who follow celebrities to take photographs of them
quandary = a state of uncertainty
ravioli = small pasta cases containing minced meat, cheese and vegetables
sphinx = an Egyptian stone figure having a lion's body and a human head
teenybopper = a young teenager who follows the latest fashions in clothes and pop music
unique = being the only one of its kind
vamoose = leave hurriedly
whippersnapper = a young and inexperienced person who is bold and overconfident
xylophone = a musical instrument played by striking a row of bars with small beaters
yucca = a plant with sword-like leaves, native to warm regions of the US and Mexico
Zuider Zee = an area of reclaimed land in The Netherlands.

Language: Fun with Words (1) – page 28

Activity B. Picture Puzzles

1 Too little, too late.
2 A friend in need.
3 Up to no good.
4 Back door.
5 Hop up, hop down.
6 All over again.

Grammar: Verbs – page 39

Activity C

1 to join together = connect
2 to leave behind = abandon
3 to make a choice = decide
4 to draw = illustrate
5 to fix or mend = repair
6 to buy = purchase
7 to find = locate
8 to say or do again = repeat

Grammar: Conjunctions – page 67

Activity C

Answer to riddle: trampoline